The
Montauk
Fault

By Herbert Mitgang

FICTION
THE MONTAUK FAULT
GET THESE MEN OUT OF THE HOT SUN
THE RETURN

BIOGRAPHY
THE FIERY TRIAL: A Life of Lincoln
THE MAN WHO RODE THE TIGER: The Life and Times of
Judge Samuel Seabury
LINCOLN AS THEY SAW HIM

CRITICISM
WORKING FOR THE READER: A Chronicle of Culture,
Literature, War and Politics in Books from the 1950s to the
Present

REPORTAGE
FREEDOM TO SEE: Television and the First Amendment

EDITOR
THE LETTERS OF CARL SANDBURG
CIVILIANS UNDER ARMS: Stars and Stripes, Civil War to
Korea
WASHINGTON, D. C., IN LINCOLN'S TIME
SPECTATOR OF AMERICA
AMERICA AT RANDOM: Topics of The Times

PLAY
MISTER LINCOLN

The Montauk Fault

A NOVEL BY

HERBERT MITGANG

ARBOR HOUSE New York

Library of Congress Catalog Card Number: 80-70744

ISBN: 0-87795-320-1

Manufactured in the United States of America

10 9 8 7 6 5 4 3 2 1

For S. M., and for a few
old friends—David Golding,
William Hogan, Abram Barkan

BE DISLOYAL. IT'S YOUR DUTY TO THE HUMAN RACE. IF
YOU HAVE TO EARN A LIVING, AND THE PRICE THEY MAKE
YOU PAY IS LOYALTY, BE A DOUBLE-AGENT—AND NEVER
LET EITHER OF THE TWO SIDES KNOW YOUR REAL NAME.
—GRAHAM GREENE, *A Sense of Reality*.

DREAMING IN AMERICA IS NO CINCH.
—SAUL BELLOW, *Humboldt's Gift*.

One

At precisely five minutes after five o'clock, on a certain sun-dappled June day in our time, the Montauk Lighthouse, which had sent forth the first reassuring signals of candlepower to thousands of hoodeyed sea captains following their stars and compasses along the North Atlantic bridgeways to America, quite suddenly developed a crack at the base of its red-and-white, candy-striped tower. The widening fissure quickly snaked up the hundred feet to the twirling three hundred and fifty thousand candlepower lamp, stopping it dead. Reversed, the half-killed beam turned downward and inward, facing on the land side, momentarily blinding the Coast Guardsmen on duty and the accidental visitors on the precipitous bluff. Then the lamp extinguished itself and shattered, sending slivers of glass shrapnel flying over the heads of the stunned onlookers below. At the same instant the electrical circuits in the crumbling tower twisted into crackling sparklers and, wires crossing, touched off the current in the powerful foghorn. Its throatclearing single bass note could be heard for miles in every direction; and, amplified, the foghorn played a mournful dirge over the scene of devastation.

As if by appointment, the twin-engined ninety-foot *Saucy Queen II*, loaded to the gunwales with meat fishermen after a long and successful trip out beyond the Montauk rip, where giant cod, pollack and haddock were caught by sonar soundings in the feeding and hiding ledges of a hundred wrecks, was sailing north by northwest directly below the lighthouse on Turtle Hill, bound for its anchorage inside Gin Beach, when what seemed almost a predestined tremor unhinged the sandstone tower and its reinforced concrete outbuildings. Gathering momentum down the eroded headland and over the permeable dune-grass, the broken lighthouse and the glacial boulders below joined forces with a primordial thundering roar and demolished the *Saucy Queen*.

The screaming fishermen were crushed on the deck or drowned as the ship splintered into steel shards and sank like a child's toy in six fathoms of bloodied water. For a long time the stench of singed electrical cables mingled with the rank oil slick that washed over the morainal sediment, clinging to the sand now blackened by the berm of the restless seas.

The aftershock rippled the surface of the ocean for several miles, reaching Ditch Plains on the Atlantic side, where whaling boats had once been surf-launched in a calmer century. Knobby surfers, seeking the ultimate wave of the dying day, got it. Their skins ripped and sanded by the overturning waves that cast them far above the shoreline, the surfers abandoned their beach haunt for months afterward. On the Block Island Sound side, the roiled waters reached almost as far as the fishing station at the point known as Promised Land, before disappearing in the endless disguise of the rhythmic tides.

The death of the sentinel at the furthermost promontory on Long Island temporarily caused confusion among pilots checking the beacon as a visual navigation aid and among captains homing in on the familiar tower as their first landfall. A vagrant fishing vessel from New Bedford turning north northeast barely avoided the flashing light in Block Island Sound and foundered in two fathoms on the Carberus Shoal. The radiobeacon at Shinnecock Light, turning for thirteen and a half seconds and silent for one and one-half seconds at two hundred and ninety-eight kilocycles, appeared to be sending forth stronger signals. To the west of where the Montauk Lighthouse had stood only moments before, near the abandoned Second World War gun emplacements that had faced out into the Atlantic mists where Nazi Germany's U-boats had roamed and preyed, radarmen from the Seven Hundred and Seventy-third Air Force Base picked the sounds of the disaster out of their monitored heavens. One of their helicopters immediately fluttered and rose, hovered over the broken bluff and the floating remains of the *Saucy Queen,* and informed Washington and the world what had happened or, more accurately, what they *thought* had happened.

According to a prearranged plan, a Coast Guard cutter was ordered to change course from normal patrolling along the Great South Bay and Fire Island Inlet and proceed to the treacherous waters off Montauk Point. The cutter turned itself into a temporary lighthouse, moving in tight circles, and occasionally fishing a drowned body out of the curling waves. At twilight, three more cutters raced to the Point and, horns and whistles piercing the air, formed a ring of blinking lights around the Atlantic skies.

The following morning, to the surprise and chagrin of jealous town and county officials, several United States Government agencies arrived in some force and sealed off the entire area from Hither Hills State Park to Montauk Point. They carried signed Federal documents authorizing them to take command of local enforcement activities. The commercial fishing fleet was prevented from raising anchor. The haul-seiners along the beaches were stopped when they tried to launch their motorized whaleboats. The bay sheriffs, a law unto themselves for decades, were told by youthful-looking scientists from the Food and Drug Administration to make sure that not a clam, not a scallop, not a crab or anything else that crawled or swam should be lifted out of the protected waters until they had determined what, if any, contamination had resulted from the Lighthouse's sudden death. A team of treasurehunters, diving near where *H.M.S. Culloden* had gone down during the Revolutionary War era, was unceremoniously ordered to quit and leave its equipment for inspection. The headquarters of the Eastern Air Command dispatched relays of helicopters to survey the damage. Even the Long Island Railroad's Toonerville trains were stopped at Amagansett; all unofficial transportation had come to a dead halt. Special agents from the National Marine Fisheries Service were flown over from Cape May and Cape Cod stations to sift through the cold ashes where electrical fires had flared for clues that might reveal the lasting effects of the disaster.

Curiously, the watch was doubled by the Coast Guard patrolling the coastal waters all around the United States. Orders went forth from the Department of Defense—a puzzling, suspicious source since it had never before exercised any jurisdiction over international mariners—to extend the two hundred mile fishing limit for vessels flying foreign flags to five hundred miles. Publicly, this was explained as a safety precaution until the exact degree of contamination could be measured: but no reason was offered why the emergency regulation covered not only the Eastern seaboard but all Southern waters and the length of the Pacific littoral. Protests were lodged by the Soviet Union and the Japanese Government on behalf of their vast fishing fleets (ever since the last sperm whales on earth had been harpooned a year before, except for a pair that aquaculturists were attempting to breed in captivity, the pressure by commercial fishermen had increased). Other foreign governments, including those from the Arab and Third World that had never so much as launched a rowboat from their landlocked borders, delivered vehement speeches in the Economic and Social Committee of the United Nations about colonialism and imperialism on the high seas.

Five hundred miles out, the gunnery officer on the

nine hundred and thirty-ton U.S.S. *Cuttlefish* ordered his crew to douse their cigarettes and bring up the ammunition from the magazine belowdecks to the locker on the bow, alongside the three-inch gun. On either side of the bridge, they locked fifty-calibre machine guns in their swiveling boltheads. Then, grinning as usual, they delicately rolled their own condoms over the tips of the naked barrels. It was an old Navy tradition: keep your powder if not your semen dry.

An hour before dawn, the chief petty officer took a three-star navigational fix. On the horizon, just outside the forbidden five hundred mile unmarked dividing line, the watch reported and then confirmed that the blips on the radarscope were three Russian trawlers, including the familiar mother ship, *Glinka*. The outlines of its electronic masts were known by sight up and down the Atlantic coastline. The *Glinka* carried enough communications gear to serve as flagship for a fleet of submarines; its crew of specialists fished only for information. The captain of the *Cuttlefish* took his mug of coffee down to the radio room and, almost routinely, reported the location of the Russian trawlers to Governor's Island in New York Harbor. An urgent response flew back from Coast Guard headquarters: Keep the *Glinka* in sight, fire a shot across her bow in case she penetrates the five hundred mile limit, do not repeat not exchange any other signals, and stand by for further orders.

That Sunday, sermons were delivered by journalists and ministers on the meaning of the demise of the Montauk Lighthouse. Both were surprisingly similar, entertaining, and ill-informed. By a coincidence, the New

York and Washington newspapers ran almost the same layouts in their feature sections—stock photographs showing lighthouses around the United States. The human interest angles were played up—people who were born in lighthouses, lived in abandoned lighthouses, their dream significance as phallic symbols, lighthouses as shining sentinels of freedom in a hostile world divided between the forces of light and darkness. Barely having time to rewrite the dailies because of their weekend deadlines, the national newsweeklies also by coincidence of editorial minds placed the same title on their Montauk stories: The Lighthouse That Failed. Timed for the Christmas trade, one of their publishing divisions began assembling an instant coffee table book about lighthouses from the Age of Homer to the Age of Edison. Researchers for the book writers looked up their favorite quotations in college notebooks by Verlaine, Rilke, Hesse and Baudelaire so that the lighthouse captions could be sprinkled with a suitable number of learned philosophical observations.

Because one of the most important dog and cat food sponsors had shifted its commercials to another network as a result of a half-point drop in ratings—confirmed by a poll and national market research among animal owners about their (the pets') mealtime and snack preferences—that Sunday a precious hour became available at an unsponsored throwaway time. The news department of the lagging network was ordered to mount a noncontroversial program that would score points for public service with the Federal Communications Commission. Standing in front of a blowup of the Montauk Lighthouse before the fall, the network's leading commentator reviewed its historic role. George Washington himself had approved the Congressional mandate to construct a lighthouse on this Atlantic bluff, despite the fact that the wealthy farmers on the Tory end of Long Island had delivered much of their provender to King George's Redcoats and Hessians. Which clearly proved why the First President was first in war, first in peace, first in the hearts of his countrymen. General Washington had predicted that the Montauk Lighthouse would stand for two hundred years; and he had come very close. Only time and the tides had caused the unfortunate demise of the world-famous landmark, the commentator declared with deep-voiced certainty, and, as the closing theme music swelled, he concluded: That's the way it was in 1795 and that's the way it was at precisely five minutes after five o'clock, last Friday.

But that was *not* the way it was.

Overlooking President Washington's freemasonry, several of the memorial services that Sunday called attention to his prescience and faith in God and country, his devotion to the Montauk Lighthouse, and to the men who put out to sea guided by the shining light of a Higher Being. At the Holy Church of St. Isidor, the assistant pastor, trying to make a good impression on his bishop, who received carbon copies of all sermons in the diocese, started with the old-fashioned words from his *Collectio Rituum:* More than watchmen wait for sunrise, let Israel wait for the Lord, He will redeem Israel from all their sinfulness.

The young pastor, who was eager to get ahead,

14

knew that his bishop regarded Pope John XXIII's liberalizing reign as an unfortunate interregnum: ecumenical language was not appreciated in the churchly boondocks. He added a few burial service lines from Paul's letter to the Romans: We are debtors, then, my brothers, but not to the flesh, if you live according to the flesh, you will die; but if by the spirit you put to death the evil deeds of the body, you will live—this is the word of the Lord. The pastor asked his parishioners to join him: *Domine, exaudi orationem meam.* O Lord, hear my prayer. *Dominus vobiscum. Et cum spiritu tuo.* The Lord be with you. And with your spirit.

The fall of the Montauk Lighthouse and the deaths of the fishermen and Coast Guardsmen, so the ministers solemnly said, could only be explained as Acts of God. But they were not: what occurred was very much an Act of Men.

Only a small group of people knew what had really happened, and why, under that pellucid sky on a day of peace in June. One in particular discovered that he was enmeshed, perhaps unwisely, in the unfolding terrors of his time.

Two

Early that spring, not long before the great lighthouse had come crashing down, a man of middle years and middle accomplishments and burdens walked north along Sixth Avenue. Sam Linkum looked up at the uniform glass windows that could not be opened by human hands in these homogenized Manhattan office towers and thought that it finally made sense to him why this street should be called by its official name, the Avenue of the Americas. Not as a tribute to the banana republics and the mineral-rich dictatorships run by brevetted South American colonels who were Washington trusties because they had studied at the Army's Command and General Staff College in Fort Leavenworth, Kansas. Rather, it was the overpowering presence on this street and on its Rockefeller Center artery of all three commercial television networks. They were, in their fashion, as American as you could get: they delivered the news of the goods between the news of the country. Their prefab products and programs were exported and admired up and down the Americas from the Panama Canal to Tierra del Fuego. And now, suddenly, he realized with a shudder that he was to be a part of it all—if he was lucky enough to be among the survivors.

Long afterward, the phrase would come back to him:

I'm a bottom line girl.

You could almost put it to music.

Linkum turned into the network's travertine-fronted entranceway. He knew that he had stepped into the right building; in the lobby stood one of Henry Moore's Family Group bronzes, lit like a shrine. The network used the sculpture as a running symbol of its boast that all the shows it sent out over the franchised national airwaves were clean, affirmative, and decently family-oriented. Linkum asked the starter for Jane Twining Delafield's floor. Group corporate—eighteen—first stop on the express. Going up, he noticed that the numbers on the buttons and the lettering in the elevator were printed in a uniform sans-serif News Gothic. The network's corporate art director went to great pains to see that all its exterior touches matched the latest type faces from advertising row. He wondered if there would be any further use for his own knowledge of printing.

"The first thing that you ought to know about me is—," Ms. Delafield said, cradling the phone like a lover in her bony shoulder cavity, "I'm a bottom line girl."

Linkum slipped into the narrow chair opposite her oval, pickled-pine desk. From here she looked to be in her carefully presented late forties, perhaps a few years

18

older, younger than he was or felt. She covered the mouthpiece again and said, "Make yourself comfortable while I get rid of this character." The buzzer from her secretary rang, informing her about a backed-up call. She juggled both, putting the first on her hold button and, at the same time, said, "Do you mind stepping outside for a sec? This one's important. Don't go away now."

Awkwardly, he got up and closed the door behind him. Standing next to the secretary's photocopying machine, he instinctively followed an old reporter's habit and read the uncovered papers being reproduced backwards. Nothing much. Through the closed door he could still hear Ms. Delafield darlinging her important caller. The buzzer commanded him back. This time he stood until she motioned him into the chair. From the glowing ash of the one already in her mouth, she lit a second Marlboro Longhorn. He declined her offered pack.

"Sorry for the interruption," Ms. Delafield said, "but that was my opposite number at Ralston Purina—the group veepee in charge of the high protein dog meal account—and they're buying one hundred and fifty minutes across-the-board on our major Evening News program, and a few documentaries thrown in if they approve of the subjects. It's our biggest buy of the season."

"Congratulations," Linkum said.

He had read in one of the business newsweeklies that Jane Twining Delafield had been put high up on the network's board of directors because her fine-sounding name gave the communications conglomerate the resonance of very Upper-Middle America, offering in one person an ethnically and sexually balanced political ticket that translated clearly into corporate signal language on Wall Street and in Washington.

But she obviously had a certain talent and enthusiasm about her new powerful role in broadcasting—and, hereafter, in what the network executives called print journalism.

"I heard you were one of the stalwarts on the newspaper, Sam," she said cozily. "Mind if I first-name you?"

"Feel free," he replied, shifting uncomfortably.

"I like your mature looks—someone with salt-and-pepper around the temples, taller than average but not too, regular features. You could probably handle an anchorman's spot."

"No thanks," he said, wincing and smiling.

Her desk buzzer blasted; she told her secretary to hold the calls. "Here's the poop," she said, looking at her wristwatch furtively. "Someone's got to mind the bottom line for us or the accountants and auditors will be running our show. So I'm elected. I didn't particularly want to take on the print end of things for the company. Between us, it's a trap. I've got plenty on my plate already. You may have heard that I won my senior stripes long before your newspaper got into The Late Troubles—"

"It's not my newspaper," Linkum interrupted. "I'm just one of the hired hands there."

"You don't have to shit-kick me. I know you're one of the heavy hitters, journalisticwise. You're one of the people I'd like to keep, if we can work out the right spot for you. I'm under orders from the company to cut the staff by twenty per cent. Everyone knows there's plenty of fat and deadwood sitting under those green eyeshades."

"I haven't seen a copyreader wear one in years," he said. "But that's not very important. Why do so many people have to be let go? Can't the conglomerate afford to keep a good staff intact?"

"Don't think I enjoy being Little Miss Hatchet Girl," she said. "But, Sam, you know as well as I do that your newspaper would have gone under if the network hadn't stepped in to save it. I know there was advertiser competition with the nets for the buck but it was much more than that, and you'd better believe it."

She waited for him to react; he kept quiet.

"Your newspaper and others like it thought that the folks out there are interested in reading about what every third-rate prime minister in London and Paris and Timbuktu had to say. And all those damn environmental and ecological and pollution stories that came out of everybody's craw. You thought you could shove news down people's throats, and make them shell out money to pay for it and, what's more, give them a daily dose of depression. There was no good news, nothing to lift the spirits. And, if I may say so, the total effect was to play into the hands of the haters of America here and our enemies on the other side."

Almost defensively, Linkum heard himself saying, "Don't you think our series last year explaining the role of the multinational corporations and this year's on the breakdown of the disarmament talks were newsworthy?"

"Kneejerk journalism, Sam. Worth maybe one piece, off Page One somewhere. That oldfashioned liberal stuff is a turnoff. Maybe not to you, but to the general public. Did those series reflect marketing research? What did your polls show?"

"We don't poll the public to find out what's news," Linkum replied, keeping his voice calm.

"Then how can you possibly know what the public wants to read—and buy? How can your advertising salesmen talk intelligently about delivering cost per thousand readers?"

"We keep the editorial side of the paper separate from the advertising side," he said. "That's been a tradition."

"Tradition will get you nowhere in the marketplace. I'm talking about this world, not the next one."

She glanced at her watch, openly this time.

He felt that he had not made himself clear or presented a very good case for the things he stood for. Hastily, he added, "We're professionals—that's what we're all about. After you've reported and edited stories for years, you know instinctively what is news, what is a publicity handout, what is a snow job from a corporate officer or government official—"

"Let me stop you right there," she said. "At our network, we don't feel superior to the American public. We don't try to impose our superior taste on theirs. We feel an obligation to tune in on them if we want them to tune in on us. You have to feel their pulse and measure the feedback. I don't know if you agree—I suspect, frankly, that you don't—but let me use the big word for our way of doing it: Democracy. That's why we call it the mass medium. Otherwise, you're an elitist. Unless you're holding your finger in the wind, you're farting in the breeze."

She did not sound like Jane Twining Delafield; but then Sam Linkum did not know his bottom line girl very well.

"Which finger?" he said, trying to make light of it.

She managed to smile sourly.

"By the way," he said, "I don't want you to get the notion that I feel superior to the readers of the paper."

"I trust we're on the same wavelength," she said. "Anyway, let's get down to the business at hand. Our plan is to fold the newspaper subsidiary into the total mix of our profit center—the leisure-time division."

"My impression is that we'd be independent," he said.

"Wrong impression," Ms. Delafield said. "The basic delivery of the news will continue to come from the network news show. After all, the anchormen and an-chorpersons have the main audiences, the big numbers. You know our slogan: You give us twenty minutes— we'll give you the United States. That's a half-hour every night, less ten minutes out for the commercials. We're going to make reading the newspaper supplementary to the network show. It will be in synch so there won't be repetition. The big thing, as I see it, and I'm open to experiment, not tradition, is that the newspaper will cover the people part of the news—how they live, where they live, the food they eat, the clothing they buy, the movies and theatres they attend, the parking places downtown—in other words, the personality stuff and the service stuff."

"And what about Washington and the rest of the world?" Linkum inquired.

"Don't worry—they'll still be there even if they don't make the nightly news or Page One. Who really gives a shit about South Africa or South America or the Securities and Exchange Commission out there in Six-pack, U.S.A.? The peasants and natives will continue to make babies while we give them free birth control devices, and nobody pays any attention to the Federal regulatory agencies, so what else is new?"

"What happens to the correspondents and bureaus —are you going to fire them all and shut them up?"

Ms. Delafield ignored Linkum's rising anger.

"We won't need both a man carrying a tape recorder and a second man next to him carrying a pencil. It doesn't add up. My first target is to get rid of duplication. My second target is to straighten out the nuts and bolts of coverage. Our current thinking is that the newspaper branch should have a regular daily section devoted to the main personalities of the moment—not the ding-a-lings but the up-front crowd, the take-charge guys and gals, the Now Generation. People can never get enough of their Cinderella stories plus their mishaps, marriages and mistresses. That's the salted peanuts for our mass audiences. What makes the ebb and flow of media communications in our—"

"You mean a whole section devoted to gossip?"

She glared at him.

"You said it—I didn't. It's a matter of semantics. You can call it gossip if that's your word for it, but not too loud. That's water-cooler chitchat. Our Research and Development surveys prefer to call it lifestyles. Wouldn't that be more appropriate—and make you feel better?"

Linkum did not answer.

"What I have in mind for you, Sam, is to run this new section. Look, I'm not saying that it would be cheap or shoddy. Give it class, make it look and sound appetizing. You know, we have one of the top corporate art directors in the game. He'll be glad to work with you on the design if I give him the signal. He's a big white-space advocate, and can help you get rid of that talking-heads, crowded-with-words appearance. What do you say?"

Linkum stalled. He did not consider words the enemy.

"I'll need some time to think it over."

"Time is a luxury that, unfortunately, we haven't got. This is a whole new ballgame, and it's batter up, not the seventh-inning stretch. Look," she confided, leaning over her desk toward him. "I haven't mentioned this up to now because I didn't want to influence your thinking but there's another ten thousand a year in it for you."

She leaned back and lit another Marlboro Longhorn and watched his face.

"Let me give it some thought," he said.

Linkum did not care to tell her that, for reasons he would share with no one and especially company strangers, the extra ten grand would indeed influence his thinking.

"Overnight?" she pressed.

And before he could reply, she added: "The leisure-time division is the glamor part of the company. You have to get off the pot because there are plenty of people —including on your newspaper—standing in line behind you. They'd jump at the chance."

She held a list of names aloft, rustling it impatiently. He did not know that such a table of organization existed for his colleagues.

"Overnight," he said, pushed into a corner. She smiled.

"Sam, you've got to know that I'm a bottom line girl. The figures have to add up in the profit and loss columns, my friend, or you don't go to press or light up the skies on the tube. But believe me, there's nothing wrong with giving and getting a little more in the pay packet. I like to give it and I like to get it. Call me first thing in the morning."

He got up and she extended her hand. For a small woman, Ms. Delafield had, just as the books of advice on corporate power mandated, a surprisingly hard grip.

"What I'd especially like to have from you is a list of ideas for the changeover issues of the newspaper— names and numbers, features that are grabbers, the key personalities swimming upstream into the public eye, and before they become everybody's property. I'm a big one for getting things down on paper so we can shake out the bummers before investing time and money."

She talked as if she knew what his answer would be.

26

Linkum felt that there was more at stake than he could articulate to the persuasive Ms. Delafield.

Although it was his day off, that evening Linkum followed his instincts and found himself wandering back to the paper. He knew that Jennie Ives would be working late, turning out her twelve hundred and fifty-word roundup of the week's unchanging changes in foreign affairs for the Sunday edition. They had what both called "sort of a date," accepting their relationship that way: two grownups hanging in there, with no-fault insurance, and no strings. If love had no strings.

It was the time he liked best, the big pause, between the chaotic miracle monent when the early edition hit the streets and rolled away forever, filled with wire-service news and analytical reports and slapped-in shorts about faraway typhoons and tsetse flies and typographical errors that with luck did not deliberately spell out dirty words, and the final edition, when the correspondents had time to update their stories across the world's time zones and the theatre and music critics filed their reviews and nobody was around except the widowers and passed-over editors and rewrite men who—for the so-called "good of the paper"—had been put on someone's shit list so long ago that no one remembered why and the deskmen and deskwomen, too, who disappeared to their lockers for a quick one, and the former bright young things from the wire services and hometown press who had lost the jiggle in their behinds while sitting it out to success in the big time and had begun to wonder what making it meant in lost chances, an hour before midnight.

Linkum waved hello to a couple of copyreaders who had become voiceless in the evening of their years; and as always he felt a twinge of guilt because they were still bent over the rows of metal beatup desks while he had moved up to wood.

The ancient graduated copyboy-receptionist handed him the early edition of the paper and they exchanged their ritual for the thousandth time: "How they hanging, Lou?" "Hanging loose, Sam." Then Lou added, "She's out to lunch—about fifteen minutes ago—in case you were going back to the Sunday section."

There were no secrets in the newsroom. With everyone's head down, everyone knew who was seeing whom, who was trying to connect, and who had scored. The rumor mills ground out the office gossip—the only news that aroused interest among the old pros. The rest was merely Page One stuff, the job.

Linkum strolled back to the weekend area, where a few of the versatile writers were busily putting together their analysis pieces for Sunday. He sensed that the two covering national metropolitan affairs were among those slated for the cut list under the new conglomerate setup. They knew that he had been talking to the network management: they had not been summoned to Ms. Delafield's throne room. For that matter, Jennie had not been tapped and told to come in for a talk, at least not yet. All three had once worked on the newsweeklies, where they had been obliged to jazz up stories and follow the shifting management party lines, and had chosen to come to the paper where they could play the news fairly straight. He had hired them himself, but now they were part of the death watch.

They looked up from their typewriters, nodded hellos the same as goodbyes, and returned to their work, heads down.

He slumped into the chair next to her desk and glanced over tomorrow's headlines: SURVEY SHOWS 13 NEUTRON NATIONS BY END OF DECADE. CITY BANKS INCREASE MORTGAGE RATE. KGB SAID TO CONTROL CZECH POLITBURO. OFFSHORE OIL BLOWOUT BLACKENS LONG ISLAND BEACHES. CIA DENIES KNOWLEDGE ITS AGENTS WIRETAPPED SENATE INVESTIGATION COMMITTEE. CHILEAN COUP PUTS NEW COLONELS IN COMMAND. PAKISTAN EXPLODES OWN ATOMIC DEVICE. CONTINENTAL DRIFT BLAMED FOR QUAKE-SLIDE IN GUATEMALA. ARAB NATIONS DEMAND WORLD BANK BILLIONS. DISARMAMENT TALKS DELAYED ANOTHER YEAR. METS LOSE.

Not much news. It looked like a light weekend.

Jennie Ives wandered into the Sunday area, balancing three containers of black coffee.

"Hi, Sam," she said. "You can have half of mine."

"You're running late," he said, quietly, sipping from her cup.

"Late for lunch, early for dinner," she said. "I've got another couple of hundred priceless words to go. Stand by for the big wrapup and tune in next week, same time and same station, gang, for two momentous moments less forty-five seconds for Purina Chows, your favorite program, *Your World and Welcome to It*."

She sounded bitter : funny-bitter. The others looked up and grinned watching for a reaction from Linkum.

He smiled, realizing that he was in the peculiar position of not wanting to say anything openly that might harm his efforts to save their jobs. "Let's give the Sunday readers a break after church and get the jokes into the script," Linkum said.

He glanced at Jennie as she wound up her foreign news piece. She was one of the few writers in the newsroom who managed to look composed instead of in a cocoon of anguish while typing against a deadline. It was one of the things he admired about her. For a woman of over-forty, she did not allow her professionalism to consume her vivacity. The light touch characterized her work, and herself.

"What's your top this week?"

"I thought I'd lead off with the Guatemalan disaster —God, five hundred people under rubble—and then swing into the Pakistan atomic thing and pair them up with the neutron bomb for everybody."

"Natural and manmade disasters?"

"That's the general idea. You're a quick study, Sam."

"I've been practicing on that story for years. Ever since Hiroshima. I have the official phrases down pat by now: More bang for the buck, first-strike capability, protective reaction, MIRV's, MARV's, AWAC's, and the rest of the family arsenal."

She handed him a carbon of her opening pages. He skimmed quickly and said, "It works. Now let's get out of here and let the world spin by itself for a while. You chaps can keep an eye on what's-his-name in the White House."

They said their goodnights and left together, walking past the midnight men still on duty and the weekend editors with compensating titles of authority who hardly saw their children except asleep or for a month on vacation—the benched players who had talked themselves into liking their anonymity because they had not made the Monday-to-Friday varsity on the paper, and the tieless hours gave them a freedom of their own.

The affair between Sam Linkum and Jennie Ives was a pretty open thing and, walking past the deskmen, they made no effort to hide their departure together.

Mannie's Place a few blocks away was still jumping with the after-theatre crowd and the midnight cowboys hustling drinks and the stray singles at the side bar who were getting a little desperate and up for grabs and the press agents and advertising space salesmen looking for live ones so they would not have to go home. Ever since Lindy's and Dinty Moore's and Bleeck's had been taken over by the conglomerate restaurant chains and turned into glorified hamburger stands for the expense-account crowd, there were not any decent places left on the West Side within striking distance of the paper. At least Mannie himself could claim a link to the past; he had been an argumentative waiter at Lindy's once who had parlayed a winning lottery ticket into a restaurant without pretensions.

They found a corner table without too much light and ordered steak sandwiches with the good Carlsberg beer that Mannie kept on tap. Nobody could overhear them here.

"How did it go—and what's she like?"

"She's a bottom line girl," he said.

"I can't tell if that's a sexy or a sexist remark."

"Neither—it's corporation chitchat. It's not your bottom, it's your bottom line that counts. The bucks—the profits—the P and L for the accountants running the show. She watches it, creatively, of course, it says here."

"And the paper?"

"What paper? You mean the print medium, don't you?"

"Stop the kidding, Sam. Where do we all stand?"

"You and I are now part of a profit center within the leisure-time division."

He reached across the table for her hand. He loved what she sometimes gloved, its honestly veined and creased character.

"Ms. Delafield has a little list, Jennie. The body count. I'm not sure who's in and who's out yet, but she says that twenty per cent of the staff will have to be let go."

"Why that many? With all the dough the network makes?"

"The paper's tradition is a dead weight if you're in the moving-image business. The look changes from season to season—"

"The image? Why, we're about the last real paper left in town that's still interested in news coverage. And you? And me?"

"She didn't mention your name, or anyone else specifically. She'll keep us all offbalance. The game of *sauve qui peut*. But they'll need the professionals, and you're the best there is."

32

"And where do you stand with Her Highness, Sam?"

"I'm in—if I can hack it on her terms. She's got some notion of turning part of the news into what she calls lifestyles. By whatever name, it's gossip. And lucky me would be put in charge of that section."

"You poor bastard."

When Jennie said it, it sounded loving instead of vulgar. She could be truthful and blunt in the same breath. It was what made her writing a reflection of herself.

"I was thinking about you and some of the others," Sam said. "The ones covered by the union contract should be able to hang in there—or get a good settlement. I've seen enough of these conglomerate takeovers to know that they'll pay you off handsomely as long as they can get you to remove your body from their building. Did you ever realize you're real estate?"

She shook her head. He ordered another round, and after they finished in silence, she whispered, "Sam, let's put the network nonsense out of your head for as long as we can. I'd like to go home now, if you don't mind."

He had waited for her to say so.

Jennie's apartment overlooking Gramercy Park was high enough to dim the roar of the buses and the coughing of the jackhammers that were always molesting the streets. The small enclave of repose between midtown and the Village was old-fashioned, deliberately romantic and private—something like Jennie herself away from the office. The brownstones fanning out into the side streets from the small park held a hundred literary associations, from Henry James to O'Henry. Sometimes as they wandered she pointed out who had lived and written which classic where in third-floor rooms, and he had kidded her, saying that it was dangerous for a mundane journalist to know too much about the American literary past, it could interfere with your daily quota of journalistic clichés. He smiled when he said it.

From the bowed windows that Jennie threw open on warm nights, you could see the twinkling of lights in the high-rises, and sometimes a moving light between the openings in the skyline turned into a jetliner, and, transported, you could imagine yourself floating in the heavens between the broken sparkle of the city.

Then it was a ritual that perhaps placed them both in the years after youth: observing the amenities, waiting for the other to make the first move. It was one of the things that kept them together and yet apart, and made of each occasion a date. The moment he crossed the threshold, Jennie reached inside his jacket and put her arms around his waist. He embraced her and pressed his mouth against her pliant, parted lips and opened his eyes so that he could see hers closed. It was a stolen moment of the most private intimacy; and, when she was breathless, her chest heaved for air, and their full bodies came together. He kissed the lids of her eyes.

"Jennie," he whispered, and, in a throaty voice, she barely said, "Sam," and their naming of their names signaled desire before lovemaking.

While she showered, he undressed and put on the silk robe that she had given to him last Christmas. Sometimes, though not always, he stayed overnight, and the robe in her closet was the symbol of their intimacy.

They lay holding each other, hanging on without moving for as long as they could, until their bodies swelled; and then, gently aware of their own rhythms, they knotted in passion. And, afterward, Sam said, "It's still the greatest invention, all the parts fitting together perfectly, working in unison," and Jennie nudged him playfully and said, "Don't make light of it, you don't have to say anything, this is my time of silence," and he reached across and embraced the center of her warmth, and listened to her heart.

"Well, let me put it more gracefully," he said, after a moment. "It's easy to get laid; it's hard to make love."

"Not for us," she said. "That's why it's so lovely."

Before falling asleep, they unloosened the thoughts darkening their minds. Jennie seemed more disturbed about his dilemma: if he could continue to separate his working and private life. For a second time, she muttered, "You poor bastard."

He did not know if she was referring to the crisis on the job, where he would have to take on a demeaning cutthroat role for the network at the newspaper or, as in the past, to his wife.

The next afternoon, he phoned Jane Twining Delafield.

"What's the verdict, Sam?"

Her voice grated his ear, and he hesitated, almost ready to kick it over and follow his real instincts. She filled the time.

"I was sitting around, cleaning up the desk. I've been studying back copies of the paper. No wonder things were rotten and the network—"

"I'll try it."

"Now you're talking, Sam. But it's going to be more than try. I'm a doer myself and I want doers working for me." She paused. "Do you want to come over and celebrate with a drink? I've got a closetful of bourbon, scotch and ice in the office fridge."

"Nope, but thanks anyway."

"Or, if you prefer imported beer, we've got a new sponsor launching a line of light beer from Hamburg. It's supposed to be the best there is—"

"I'm busy."

"I heard you the first time," she replied, with an edge to her voice. "Have you got the list of ideas I asked you to draw up?"

"Not yet—but I'll have them in due time."

"In due time," she said, mimicking him. "Like Monday morning, first thing?"

"Probably." And, for his own amusement, he added, "Have a nice weekend."

He hung up. Over the years he had seen a lot of titles come and go—assistant managing editors and crony deputies and favorite sons with invented corporate spots. He had learned to cool his temper and, if riding high himself that day, even to express a touch of sorrow for the bush-leaguers when they struck out. The gag around the shop was to be nice to the copyboy, he could grow up to be your boss. That went in spades for the networks, where energy was at least as admired as ability, and bland, youthful executives were often picked because they were thought to be on the same wavelength as those at whom the commercials were aimed.

"Who do you like in this profession?" Jennie had once asked him when he was berating one of their colleagues, and Sam, puzzled by his own anger, finally said, "The professionals."

That Saturday afternoon, as he had done for the past seven years, Linkum rented a small Plymouth on the weekend discount rate and drove along Northern Boulevard in Queens, past the storefront churches and franchises selling junk food to go and the homogenized shopping malls, until the roadway began to turn country-like, where the two-family garden apartments of the strivers opened up into the sod fields and fancy farmstands selling cheese from France, on past the hidden estates of the heirs of the fenced-in, *nouveau* strugglers who only used the old places on weekends, going from the slurbs to the urbs in little over an hour—a journey across a generation.

The green directional signs pointed out the names on the land, the sole reminders of an Indian and Colonial heritage that had been crushed beneath the blades of the bulldozers. He played his little game of guessing the sequence in order: Half Hollow Hills, Wyandanch, Fort Salonga, Ronkonkoma and Cold Spring Harbor, mixing them up because his mind was not on the game. Alone as always on this journey, he murmured the names aloud above the drone of the roadway. Then he twirled the radio dial, searching for a foreign-language station where he could try to follow what was being said between the ethnic music and messages. Picking sounds out of the blue: that, too, was a game calling up memories of short-wave receivers during chilling, companionable wartime nights in the clandestine hills when he was in counter-intelligence.

He turned off and under the roadway toward the tree-fringed Thornhill Residence. It stood high on a point overlooking Long Island Sound with nothing to indicate what the Residence was used for. When the getting and taking were good before the Great War earlier in the century, a Morgan Bank partner had raided a chateau and a half in Normandy and transported the stones to build a forty-room cottage. Dying and not sure if his temporal activities as a moneylender would bring him a favored place in the next world, he had bequeathed the windy cottage to the Episcopalian Church to hedge his bets and lower his taxes. After a few years of high heating costs, the deacons had unloaded it on an investment conglomerate of surgeons and orthodontists, who converted the estate into a private facility for emotionally disturbed adults.

Linkum parked the car and glanced around the grounds. Sometimes, Elena ventured outside alone. Instinctively, she knew the hour and the day in the week when he would pull up on the crushed bluestone. But she knew little else.

Walking past the porte-cochère, he entered the office and asked the nurse on duty how his wife was today.

"Very well," the nurse said. "Could you give me the spelling again, sir?"

"Elena Linkum. It's Room Eighteen, on the first floor facing the Sound."

The nurses at the Thornhill Residence were accommodating. This one was new. But she knew that the "residents," as the patients were referred to, were all doing very well.

"They're having their lunch now," the nurse said, "but they should be taken back to their quarters shortly. Some of them like to have their lunch early on weekends, I don't know why—"

"Because they want to spend time with relatives and visitors, that's why."

"They do have hearty breakfasts, sir."

"To be sure," Linkum said, impatiently. "Can I see her medical report for this week?"

"They should be ready shortly," the nurse replied. "Dr. Kellerman is in his office filling them out now."

"In that case, I'll ask him myself and save time."

He brushed past her and entered the adjacent office.

Dr. Kellerman looked up in surprise, and then matched the face with the patient.

"How are things at the paper, Linkum? Still knocking the medical profession?" He chuckled. "Never mind. Just came down from seeing your wife. She's been a good girl this week."

Once last year, he had blown up when Kellerman had called Elena "a good girl," but he knew it was only a manner of speaking, his way of reassuring relatives. He had checked out Kellerman with a psychiatrist friend he trusted, and the report had come back that he was an oddball but thorough and respected.

"Any change?"

He had asked the same question a hundred times, knowing the answer.

"Vital signs are all tip-top. She's a healthy woman for her age. Except, of course, for her condition."

"No problem about taking her for a little drive, then?"

"A walk, a drive—do her a world of good. If there's ever going to be a snaparound, what counts is a familiar face from the past that'll touch off something in her head. But keep it light—nothing that will aggravate her. Don't press, it won't do any good."

He walked up the flight of stairs and tapped gently on the keyless door. She turned away from the window and the view of the gently rolling Sound. Elena appeared to smile at him: her eyes were not frightened today. He said, "Hello, Elena," but her expression did not change. He helped her into a sweater. They walked to the car and he buckled and locked her in, like a child. Then he drove slowly for a few miles to a public park that faced the water, and they sat on a bench on the far end of the parking lot, away from other visitors. He found himself going through his ritual, trying to ignite her volatile mind:

"Hello, Elena, this is Sam, your husband. I hope you are feeling well today. I hope you are happy. The doctor told me that you are in good health. I hope you are eating your meals regularly even if you are not always hungry. Would you like to read a book or a magazine? You used to enjoy reading. Perhaps, perhaps you can look at a pretty picture book. You can do so in private, if you wish. In your own private room. Nobody will take your room away from you. Next week, I will bring you another pretty picture book. Do you hear me?"

Her eyes stared at him, unmoved but without hurt behind them. He reached for her hand and squeezed it lightly. She did not return the pressure but allowed him to hold it. They sat there quietly. Nothing had changed; nothing.

Elena Linkum. Elena Florio, the golden girl from Palermo that he had persuaded to leave the university and marry him. They had come to the States after the war—their war, the good war, at least one they believed in—and had been caught up in the excitement and idealism of the times. They had been happy and in love and proud of each other in the marriage: she, the foreign girl growing into womanhood and getting her degree in literature and then teaching emotionally troubled youngsters, and he, plugging away evenings and weekends by writing extra pieces on his own and making a small name for himself in the world of fact journalism and then being plucked out for higher places in the bigtime press, but still, he hoped, respected by old friends.

With some difficulty, they had a son, the only child the almond-faced golden girl would ever be able to have, the doctor said, but they both felt blessed. They called him Antonio, after her father, because Sam wanted the youth to be aware of his half-Mediterranean heritage while growing up in America. Tony resembled his mother. The fair-haired boy grew into manhood, became a scholar even while the university he attended was in turmoil, and then was caught in the draft.

It was another war, and the Nixon Administration needed more bodies for its body counts and visions of imposing the American style of life on the world, all the way to Southeast Asia. Antonio Linkum might have done the honorable thing by running away, as his father once had done the honorable thing by enlisting. Instead, some moral streak in his nature prevented him from making another young man go in his place. It would only be twelve months out of his life and then he could continue in graduate school, and please don't worry, nothing bad is going to happen. He was hit by napalm, accidentally, in a firebombing along the Cambodian border when that charred country was invaded. It took Sam months of enquiries through the Washington office of his newspaper to learn that his son had been killed by American helicopters on an unnamed hill known only by its number on a field map. Graves Registration shipped him home and said that, under the circumstances, no identification was advisable. They allowed him to be buried at the Long Island military cemetary in Farmingdale, in a neat new section reserved for Vietnam casualties. Months later, a Purple Heart arrived by mail.

Every Sunday morning, during the next year, Elena and Sam Linkum had an unspoken pact to visit their son's grave. The week built up to the day. The Graves Registration officials, courteous smiles permanently locked in their teeth, supplied plastic flower wreaths, free of charge, which never died. Instead, they brought fresh flowers from the city—flowers that wilted and died, silently without napalm, unlike their son.

Between husband and wife, nothing changed. But

both found themselves guilty when making love. Somehow finding pleasure in their own living flesh now seemed selfish. In the darkness of the long wakeful nights, they entwined their arms but seldom consummated the desires of their craving bodies.

There was a hole in their hearts. Sam had the distractions of his work; Elena, blank thinking time. She drifted far away into the past. It was something the series of doctors never could explain clearly. Her depression did not subside with the passage of the years. Fearful of her condition, Sam hired a companion to look after her. Elena's voice grew smaller and smaller and then she stopped speaking altogether. The doctors advised him to put her in the private Thornhill Residence where she could be "safe and comfortable," the phrase they used to mask the fact that she might be suicidal.

And, now, he visited her, alone each time, his own unspoken pact with himself. Once she had accompanied him to their son's gravesite—almost as experiment to see if the shock of recognition would arouse her from the inner world of silence. It was a disastrous effort. She looked at the gravestone, the almost-anonymous marker lined up in file with the others who had died in Vietnam on some forgotten jungle path, screamed once, and sank to the ground. For the next month, whenever he visited Elena, her sobs and shivering body brought tears to Sam's eyes. The golden girl from Palermo had died with her son.

Sam Linkum's friends told him that he had to try to rebuild his own life, if only to keep Elena going. And he plunged into his work more intensively. He had to—the monthly bill for Elena's maintenance took the greater part of his salary. The extra ten thousand a year could get him out of the one-room studio he lived in and into a small apartment. He hated to write and sleep within the same four walls.

In the newspaper office that Monday, Linkum shuffled the changing personality supplements from all over the country. American journalism seemed to be turning into one long gossip column. He wondered: Are they crazy—or am I incapable of keeping up? He knew that he would have to strike some sort of balance between his approach to the news and the public and Ms. Delafield's orders to give "them" what they wanted to see or read somewhere "out there" where the mentally unwashed supposedly dwelled. He would have to please his masters and, if possible, himself.

The intercom buzzed and lit up a light on his desk. The conglomerate on the Avenue of the Americas had wasted no time installing a hot line to its newspaper subsidiary.

"Sam?"

It was Herself.

"Glad you're brighteyed and bushytailed—and that you also haul in your ass early. It's me, Jane."

"I know," he said. "And good morning to you."

"Did you have a riotous weekend?"

"It was fair."

"That sounds terrible."

"Terrible is an accurate description, too."

"Well, so much for the amenities," Ms. Delafield

said. "I was hoping that you'd say you were working your keester off for me, metaphorically speaking, this weekend."

"How was your weekend?" he asked, trying to distract her.

Maybe he could handle her after all by toying with her vanity.

"Riotous, more or less," she said demurely. "Too bad we couldn't have connected."

He let that one pass.

"Why don't you hop a cab and come crosstown for a second breakfast—or maybe it's your first—in my office? I'm better face-to-face. And that way you can't hide behind the telephone."

"I was just about to roll a piece of paper into the typewriter and set down the list of ideas you wanted."

"Oh, aren't they ready? What have you done for me lately?"

"Jane, has anyone ever told you that you leave no stone or cliché unturned?"

"Come off it, friend—I know when I'm trying to be kidded to go on the defensive."

"I was merely trying to—"

"Cut the shit, Sambo," Ms. Delafield said. "I've handled masters."

For a moment there was dead air; and then he decided to blink first. Maybe that's what made her a winner in the corporate hierarchy, that and the constant surprise of her dirty mouth when her primness cracked and she was being one of the boys. It showed that she could hang tough on the bottom line.

"I'll be over in an hour with the list of ideas," he said.

"I'll be here."

He could feel the icicles dangling on the intercom.

Maybe he should have refrained from making the wisecrack about the clichés she spouted with such apparent certainty. Maybe the rules of the game permitted only familiarity from the top down. They owned the ball and the ballpark.

He walked instead of taxied crosstown, letting the air clear his head, and entered the network headquarters. Something about the prizewinning building felt wrong. This time he suddenly realized why: the place was antiseptic and so were the people working behind the uniformly clean desks. The prints on the walls were color-tuned to the furniture: art by decorator's orders. There were no wisecracking bulletin boards, no graffiti in the johns. Everybody had such white teeth, capped under the company's dental plan, and they tended to permanent smiles, like the funeral officials who handed you the flag that had been draped over your son's aluminum casket and the plastic wreaths at the Graves Registration building in Farmingdale.

Ms. Delafield was caressing her telephone in her shoulder cavity when he was ushered in. She waved him into the chair next to her desk. Without hanging up, she wiggled her fingers to signal him to pass her his list. He saved a carbon for himself. She talked over the phone and read his ideas at the same time.

When she finally hung up, Linkum asked her if she wanted him to expand on any of his ideas.

"I can read," she said.

Quickly, her hand grazed over the list. She marked each one with a "B" or a "G"—in thick red grease crayon.

"What does that mean?"

"Seven 'Bummers' and three 'Grabbers.' Not exactly a passing grade."

He mumbled that his list did not pretend to be the last word and that he was prepared to come up with other ideas.

"Let's get on the same wavelength first," Ms. Delafield said. "American military presence in Europe after decades—so what else is new? Regulatory agencies in Washington that affect your daily life? A turnoff if ever I saw one. You know, they're no-no's—one of them regulates broadcasting and another the food and drug commercials indirectly. The report from four cities in different sections of the country? A possible on a very rainy day—but hardly primetime reading. Okay on the three cultural personalities coming up in film, theatre and television but save me from the one on promising new novelists—I call them all belly-button contemplators."

"I think I get what you're driving at," Linkum said.

"Do you—honestly?"

"Honestly? You know how to hurt a guy, don't you?"

"That's better," she said, triumphantly. "Look, Sam, your section is called *Lifestyles*. It's got to have ballsy stuff that bounces off the first page, not the first page itself. Lifemanship, livingmanship, people with a capital P. I think it can work, Sam, if you'll only adjust your sights. Defense, death, taxes and all the Lo! the poor Indian!—theirs or ours—stuff are good for headlines, paragraphs and one-liners. Why not have some laughs? And why must all the news about America be so downbeat, why must all you print journalists want to shit on your own country?"

"Just the bullshit part of it," he said.

"It might do you some good if you looked at our network's *Good News Hour* that's on every Sunday afternoon."

"I've seen it—once."

"And—?"

"No comment."

"Well, wiseass, it's good enough for the *Reader's Digest.* When you can come up with their circulation numbers, then you can feel free to ignore the general reader and pull your own puddin.'"

"You have a way with words, Jane."

Ms. Delafield beamed.

Then she reached into her embossed leather folder marked "Newspaper Subsidiary" and waved a list in front of Linkum.

"I've got some ideas, too," she said, casually, and then passed him a two-page memorandum. "This is my list—the twenty people who have to be out under the new formula. Shall I tell them or will you?"

He studied the names, slowly. Jennie Ives was among them. Was there a systematic approach to the selection of those about to lose their jobs or was it all done by the numbers? He couldn't make it out.

"I told you what I thought of yours—what do you think of mine?" She seemed to be challenging, taunting him.

"I don't get it," he said, "except that most of the people on your list are the seasoned veterans on the paper."

"You mean the high-paid staffers," she said. "The over-forty types with the least flexibility and the most dough. The most costly to us."

"Well, that explains something," he said. "It's not just alphabetical—but that doesn't mean it won't hurt as much."

"We'll abide by any contracts, of course, and be generous on severance pay. The main thing is, I've got to move bodies out of the real estate. But I've explained that to you before. You have to do radical surgery to save the corpse." She paused. "Are there any names you'd like to add—or substitute?"

He smelled a rat, a rat trap, a piece of cheese for him to snap at. Still, he couldn't resist.

"I notice three of the best pros on the weekly news analysis staff—Willy Holmes, Dave Golden, and Jennie Ives—are on your shit list—"

"Correction, friend—cut list," she broke in. "Nothing personal with me. How about you?"

If she knew anything about his relationship with Jennie, she wasn't letting on—and he did not intend to give her any ammunition. Under the guise of toughness, she could be vindictive. If there was any chance at all of saving Jennie and the other professionals who were over-age in rank and experience, he sensed that the worst way would be to appeal to her better instincts.

"No, I admire all of these people and hired half of them. I wouldn't know where to begin—they're all, as you say, personal."

"So be it—"

"I just hope that when you discover the dimensions of putting out a newspaper section the professionals won't be penalized."

It was all that he wanted to say—for the moment.

"You haven't answered my other question," she said. "Shall you tell them or do you want me to?"

He wondered for an instant which would be best, for them, which would be most direct without any game-playing.

"I think you should get to know them—even leaving," he said. "It's your list. You tell them."

Simultaneously, the intercom buzzed and the push-button panel phone on her desk rang. One obviously came from a higher-up, the other from an equal. Into the intercom she poured thick sweet cream, into the telephone slightly curdled skim milk.

Linkum had lost her to the communications conglomerate.

While she fondled and stroked the wired gadgets like a vibrator, he got up and started for the door. She cupped her hands over both mouthpieces to shut out her world for a moment.

"Let's continue our dialogue on the direction of *Lifestyles* over dinner tonight—if you're free this time," she said, lowering her voice. She was telling him or ordering him, he couldn't quite tell which. "And, Sam," she added, smiling through her clenched teeth, "try to come up with a shitpotful of ideas by then."

By the time the Muzaked elevator opened on the ground floor of the network headquarters, Linkum had made up his mind. He glanced around the lobby at the corporate teeth: neither an idea nor a germ was safe here. It was only a matter of time and method: either they broke your balls or your spirit. They could do it with a kind word or with an extra ten grand. He didn't want to wait around to find out which was worse to take, the flattery or the easy coin of their realm.

Striding crosstown back to the newspaper office, Linkum felt lightheaded. He traded the ritual words with the old copyboy-receptionist: "How they hanging, Lou?" "Hanging loose, Sam." That familiarity bore no price tag.

As he walked past the desks in the big newsroom, Linkum avoided the eyes of those on the cut list. He wondered if it showed in the tense, fear-ridden atmosphere. Several of the editors waved hellos with their dark-lead pencils, not pressing him with questions. He waved in return, putting up a cheerful front, but not wishing to make it appear too cheerful. Jennie looked up and smiled enigmatically. If anything showed, Jennie would see it; she could strip away sham, including his.

After closing his office door, he picked up the phone and dialed Ms. Delafield's number. Before connecting, he hung up and instead hit the button on the intercom:

it had to work in both directions. His lit up; crosstown on the eighteenth floor, hers did, too.

"Sam?" he heard her say.

"I have a message for Ms. Delafield."

"I'm on, Sam—it's me, Jane."

He ignored her and floated his words in the wired air between them. "This is Sam Linkum. I have a message for Jane Twining Delafield, senior vice president in charge of the newspaper subsidiary, leisure-time profit center division of the network."

"What the hell is this all about?"

He said what had been stored up—slowly, measuring out his words:

"First, tell Ms. Delafield to have the bottom line department mail my severance pay check to my home as of my last day—yesterday. And, second, will you tell Ms. Delafield that the former editor of the *Lifestyles* gossip section has a final message for her: Go fuck the paper yourself."

Three

"**J**ESUS H. CHRIST!" snorted Henry H. Chorley. "Not Sam Linkum! It's out of character—it doesn't sound like my boy. I don't believe it."

The six-foot-five, two hundred and sixty-pound civilian director of the United States Air Force Security Service (USAFSS) untangled his legs from the top of his souvenir-strewn desk, knocking over the cut-down seventy-five millimeter shell case that served as the ashtray for his cigar. "Sloppy slob," he muttered in self-deprecation, retrieving the Romeo y Julieta that had begun to burn another hole in his personal Persian rug. He brushed the fine gray ashes back into the shell case and lovingly relit the cigar with a wooden match. "That friggin Castro still makes the best heaters," he said to himself, rolling the stub around his mouth, then blowing two perfect smoke rings through his puckered lips.

Chorley took the newspaper over to the light of his double-windowed corner room—3224-AF on the second level of the Pentagon's outer ring on the Arlington side. He ranked; it was right down the hall from the four-star chief of staff. That counted in more ways than one: whenever he wanted to get the general's ear for a confidence that concerned the rival services and could not be committed to paper, he timed his piss call to coincide with the big man's. Even at the Pentagon, you had to have two stars and above or simulated civilian rank to take a leak in private.

"It's fucking fishy," Chorley said aloud, shaking his head. He reread the paragraph in the *Washington Star*'s gossipy "intelligencer" column. "Discharged because of quote a difference of opinion about new newspaper format but under amicable conditions unquote? What the hell is that supposed to mean? Linkum's the Rock of Gib. Great Wall of China. Sphinx and Pyramids at Giza. Solid —one of the best. It makes no sense—and sounds like a royal screwing."

Chorley put down the newspaper and picked up the field binoculars on the window ledge, sweeping them around Washington. Or, as one of the cynical journalists had once explained to him, "the nation's capital," the phrase used by the amateurs to avoid the terrible sin of repeating "Washington" in the same breath or story. After all his years at the Pentagon, in and out of uniform, he was still thrilled when the familiar landmarks and monuments swam into sight across the Potomac.

But now a troubled look cast its shadow across Henry H. Chorley's face. The night before his own man in ELINT (Electronic Warfare) had picked up and decoded part of a signal that confirmed two other messages that had been plucked out of the warring air in the past month. The first was from a Soviet trawler stationed off Rota, the Spanish-American base where the nuclear submarines refueled before venturing out into the Atlantic and across the Mediterranean; the second came from the *Glinka*, the sophisticated Soviet mother ship on station a few miles beyond United States territorial waters, off Montauk Point on Long Island.

As head of USAFSS, Chorley had shared the information with only two others at the Pentagon—his opposite numbers in ASA (the Army Security Agency) and NSG (the Navy Security Group). He decided against putting it down on paper—even in a "top secret-eyes only" memorandum. Security, of course, was one reason but, even more compelling, he did not quite know how to make sense in a rational way of what he suspected without sounding as if he had become touched in the head by reading too many science fiction stories.

Nevertheless, he decided to tell his two colleagues almost as much as he knew: the Russians were experimenting with—perhaps had already perfected—an incredible (no: its very simplicity made it all too believable) new means of destruction that stood outside the bounds of conventional or nuclear weaponry. It could alter the very earth they stood on. It could occur like a natural disaster—unsuspected and confusing. Therefore, it would be impossible to control through routine talks around a disarmament table.

But a "natural disaster" weapon was no Soviet monopoly. Chorley wondered: how does theirs compare to ours in destructive force? Was theirs detectable; controllable? Both sides had lasers to trigger their weapons from afar by beams of powerful light waves; both sides had satellites circling the globe for surveillance of each other's land masses and bodies of water. He knew the Chemical Warfare boys at the Pentagon were keeping their big one under wraps for a few more weeks before testing it under real conditions.

In the two-star john over on the Army side, the ChemWar general had boasted, "Did you ever hear of a lake, a water supply, disappearing off the face of the earth?" That was all he would disclose but he promised to invite Chorley to see his forthcoming demonstration "somewhere in the Pacific Northwest." ELINT had picked up bits and pieces about the Soviet counterpart weapon; no question of its existence. What he had to know was how much his opposite number in Moscow knew about the American weapon and, equally important, if their triggermen were taking its consequences seriously.

Chorley snapped his fingers, alerting himself. It was one of his harmless ticks, but it offended some people who did not realize that he did so not to command but to signal one of his brainstorms.

"Maryjane!" he shouted through his closed door. "Haul ass and bring your book, too." His well-rounded new secretary—he wore them out, one way or another, every six months—teetered into his office on spiked heels. "How come all you girls from Agnes Scott College have two first names?" "Because it's much more interesting to have two of everything, don't you think?"

"Touché!" Flirting and coffee breaks helped to get the day started and kept the Pentagon in fighting trim.

"Get me a gent in New York name of Sam Linkum," Chorley said, spelling out the name. "You do it right here, not through one of the nosey operators. Shouldn't be more than one Linkum in Manhattan. Once you get him, tune us in outside at your own desk when I buzz you and take notes of what we say."

While her hands were busy dialing, Chorley's were busy rubbing. "You've got lovely cheeks, honey," he said. She gyrated in response. "Two of everything," she said, batting her eyelashes. "Ain't you the honeypot," Chorley said.

"I've got Mr. Linkum on the line, sir," Maryjane said, switching to her official government voice. Among her other talents, she was also very polite. He disengaged his roving hands with a final pat and signaled her that he wanted to be alone in his office.

"Sam? Hap Chorley here. Yeah, your old asshole buddy! Calling from the Pentagon. Never left home. What's this horseshit I've been reading about you? No, you can bet your sweet ass I don't believe everything I read in the Washington papers. Especially when they write about another newspaperman. I figure you guys are as big rivals as the generals and admirals right here. Look, Sam, I've got a helluva notion for you but I don't want to talk about it over the phone. You're out of work, right? I want you to get your ass on the ten o'clock shuttle this a. m. and I'll have my driver meet you. Unless you're in a hurry and you want me to send a fighter plane and then chopper you over here for a landing in my frontyard? No, I'm not kidding. All it takes is one phone call from me—I've got a small private air force that can pick you up and dump you off anywhere in the world, almost. You'd have to ride piggyback. Okay, I don't blame you. You'll see what's the rush when you get here. Now, drop your cock and grab an overnight bag. Don't worry, my driver will spot you as you're getting off the shuttle. See you for lunch here, old buddy."

He summoned his secretary. "You forgot to buzz me, but I took it all down anyway," she said. "Forget it," he said. "I decided to bring him down here for a face-to-face. We just shot the breeze so just shred your notes. Now, honey, you can do this for me. Get me the file on Samuel (No Middle Initial) Linkum. I've seen it in the last five years. Under the ex-agents, going way back to the Second World War. There's a more current photograph of him in the file which, of course, he doesn't know about. Give a copy of his picture to our driver so he can spot him as he gets off the shuttle. Now, I want you to bring me the Linkum file yourself—citations, personal life, current activities and salary, name of our contact on his newspaper if it isn't there already, cross-references to other agencies, the works. One more little thing: Don't tell the girls in the cafeteria, honey."

"Mr. Linkum, may I help you with your bag?"

By the time his foot touched the last step of the plane's ramp, Linkum had been singled out and escorted to the Air Force blue Mercury. When the driver deposited him at the Arlington entranceway, Maryjane awaited him. "Here's your pass, sir," she said. "My boss,

Mr. Chorley, is surely looking forward to seeing you."
He followed her wiggling backside through the maze of
corridors. "Hap Chorley and I are very old friends," he
said. "We go back four wars ago." "Isn't that charming,"
she said. "Calling him Hap."

Chorley greeted him with a bear hug. "Sam, old
cock, you're looking great—I'd recognize you on the
street, anywhere. We got a lot to catch up on."
He turned to his secretary. "Maryjane, set us up for
lunch at the two-star dining room and then take a long
one for yourself."
After she closed the door, Linkum said, "I see you're
still an ass man, Hap, and that they're getting younger."
Chorley grinned.
"You know, you're one of the few people who uses
my old nickname. They don't know it around here. It's
part of our old connection, right, Sam?"
Chorley had the same front initials as one of his
heroes, General of the Army Henry H. Arnold, so he
was pleased to be Hap, too. The legendary Arnold had
run the Air Force when it was still called the Air Corps,
in the years when they bombed Tojo's Tokyo and Hitler's Berlin instead of villages and ricefields in Vietnam
and Cambodia.
"I haven't seen that *Washington Star* piece about me,"
Linkum said. Chorley handed him the "intelligencer"
column, and asked, "Is fifty per cent of it accurate?"
"Well, I'd say that fifty per cent of it is inaccurate,"
Linkum replied. "I'm out—that's true. But the rest of it
is horseshit. It wasn't under so-called amicable circum-

stances—I was sore as hell. So were they. And I wasn't fired—I quit. That's the most important part, to me—at least it was my decision to walk out."

"They got to the public relations machine first?"

They own it."

"Fuckers," Chorley said, sympathetically. "I knew that no one was kicking you out for any good reason. I know what an old pro you are, the lives you saved—including mine when we were with the Maquis in Corsica and the S.S. found our printing press—"

"Ancient history, Hap."

"Not to me, Sam."

For the first time since seeing each other, they stared at themselves and into their pasts. Both drifted away for a moment: into the Atlas Mountains of Morocco, buying the loyalty of the A-rab chieftans who played for the highest bidders . . . the linkup with the Italian partisans north of Florence, brave men going to battle in brown-and-white sports shoes . . . making contact with the underground fighters in Corsica who risked their necks to save American downed fliers . . . dropping by parachute at night near a small airfield lit by flares along the Gulf of Corinth, working with the partisans to disarm the Krupp mines before liberating Athens.

It was all there, unspoken now, difficult to forget.

In the dining room reserved for major generals and up, waited on by enlisted men, they ate South African lobster tails and Argentinean steaks for less than two dollars each. "No wonder the national defense budget has gone crazy," Linkum said. "You're eating high off the hog at Big Mac hamburger prices." Chorley poked him playfully. "Just a little surplus chow to keep our client-states happy. You can have seconds for free if you've got space." Linkum winced, and Chorley said, "Come on back to my office for the *pièce de résistance*."

Hap Chorley left word that he was not in to anyone but his chief of staff. He locked the door behind him.

"I can't offer you a joint on government property," he said, "and I wouldn't want to—not when I've got these." Chorley opened his humidor lovingly. "Romeo y Julieta—the best. I have a connection with a friend at the Cuban mission to the United Nations. We've got a deal going: he promised not to fire any missiles at Miami Beach and I promised not to bomb his tobacco leaf at Santa Clara." He yanked the safety matches out of Linkum's hand. "You've got to use a wooden match—don't louse up the flavor." He lit Linkum's Havana cigar and his own, and then pressed a handful into his friend's jacket.

"Jesus, it's good to see you, Sam, and thanks for coming here quickly without asking questions."

"I do have a question, Hap. Nice trick you pulled at the airport. Congratulations—how did you bring it off?"

"What do you mean?" Chorley said innocently.

"The photograph of me, pal—is it a recent one?"

"Oh, that," Chorley said sheepishly, but quickly recovered. "Didn't it make you feel like a bigshot, being greeted and singled out the moment you stepped off the plane?"

"No. Actually, it was sort of embarrassing."

"Well, we like to keep up with the progress of our old friends and former agents."

"Hap, do you remember an old phrase that we used to use when we played poker in Sicily during those long nights waiting for the supply drops? Hit me—but don't shit me."

Chorley laughed.

"I still use it. Okay, if I tell you do you promise not to spill the beans to my opposite number in Moscow?"

"Cross my heart. If I do, you can have your cigars back."

"All right, you guessed it—my driver did have your picture. I'll tell you more because I'm going to have to take you into my confidence. As a matter of fact, we have three recent photographs in your A-2 file. One was easy —a copy of your passport mug shot. The second wasn't hard to get either—a copy of your ID picture that's in the personnel records at the network. We get very good cooperation from the top people at your former place of work. The third one we shot ourselves—"

"That's the only one that interests me," Linkum broke in. "What's the game?"

"—Outside a restaurant called Mannie's Place, where you, as they say, frequently lunch. With a tele-photo lens. Want me to go on?"

"Hap, what right have you got to sneak a shot of me? I thought all that domestic intelligence ended a few years ago when they caught the CIA setting up that Senator on the appropriations committee."

"We're not the CIA, Sam. We play hardball."

"Even with one of your ex-agents? And keeping an updated file on me? What the fuck for?"

"Sam, you brought this one on yourself."

"I invited you to spy on my private life?"

"Indirectly—but you asked for it. And I wouldn't be surprised if you've forgotten it by now."

Linkum looked puzzled.

"Okay, I won't keep you dangling," Chorley said. "It was the letter you sent a couple of years ago to the Guardi Art Company, Box 499, in Arlington, Virginia."

"Are you kidding, Hap?" He shook his head. "You did a whole workup on me because of that letter? You guys must be seeing spooks under your own beds."

And then Linkum was laughing and Chorley joined him, the rolls in his stomach dancing a jig.

"So you bastards got my letter after all," Linkum said. "I should have suspected as much. Causing headaches for the citizenry at home is still the name of the espionage game."

"Don't get fancy, Sam, you're not writing a column. And don't believe everything you read about us. You should have known that we had to follow up that letter. How come you sent it in the first place?"

"Would you believe it if I told you it was a lark?"

"Not really."

Chorley took a copy out of his file. He read the letter aloud: " 'Dear Sirs: I am interested in receiving literature about the art sold by the Guardi Art Company.' " The envelope—supposedly unopened—had been returned with the usual postmaster's stamp reading: "Address Unknown."

The "Guardi Art Company" was the name of the mail drop that Linkum had used during the war to circumvent intervening channels when necessary so that his information reached the head of Air Corps intelligence. The box number had been assigned to him; he had been given the option of naming his own fictitious company. And so, an amateur student of art and avid museumgoer, he had chosen his favorite painter of Venetian landscapes and lagoonscapes, Francesco Guardi, who could create on one canvas scores of tiny, animated figures along the canals by mere suggestions of white paint.

"Well, it was only for laughs—plus, I suppose, curiosity, nostalgia, whatever you want to call it. I had just been looking at a favorite Guardi at the Isabella Stewart Gardner Museum in Boston, so I decided to do it for fun. But, I never expected anyone—you, especially, old cock —to make a federal case of it, to tail me to Mannie's Place, sneak shots of me, maybe look into my personal life—"

"I didn't do it—you did, Sam. Guardi Art Company! You were asking for it. Anyway, I'm very glad it happened. It's one of the reasons I got you here—but it wasn't the main one."

Henry H. Chorley, director of USAFSS, watched the smoke rings from his Romeo y Julieta pursue each other like fighter planes maneuvering to gain altitude before disappearing in the clouds. Lowering his voice to emphasize the seriousness and privacy of his thoughts, he stared at Samuel (No Middle Initial) Linkum, and said:

"I have a job for you—an assignment."

Linkum looked at him, surprised, but saying nothing.

Chorley continued, "Sam, it's a bigger job and a helluva lot more important than anything you've ever done or ever could do for your newspaper—or even for your late bosses at the network."

Linkum still didn't react.

"Bigger than anything either of us did during our war. Bigger than anything that has crossed my desk in or out of uniform since at least the Berlin Airlift."

Linkum said, "Are you serious about asking *me?*" He pointed to the file on Chorley's desk. "Have you kept track of what I've been saying and writing, going back to the Vietnam War? You haven't done your homework, Hap."

"I've done my homework. Better still, I know my man."

"I'm not sure you do. It's not just what I've written because there's a certain amount of self-restraint and cooling it in print. It's how I *feel.* You know me as your old asshole buddy but times have changed, wars have changed, and I can tell you that I'm a different guy than the one you knew."

"All right, how do you feel?"

"That where I'm sitting is the enemy camp. No," he quickly added, "I don't mean you personally. I have as much faith in you as a person as you apparently have in me. I'm talking about the Pentagon and what it represents. Do you know—does your file on me show—that my son bought it in the Nam?"

"Yes, I do, but that's not in your file. I learned about

your boy when we were investigating the incident of napalming some of our own troops from the air. We looked into every one of those incidents to try to avoid them later. Accidents can happen flying at eight hundred miles an hour. I don't excuse them. I'm sorry now that I didn't write to you and your wife. Actually, I did but I tore up the letter. I thought that anything coming from the Pentagon, even from an old friend, would be taken the wrong way."

Linkum said, "You could have sent it, coming from you we would have understood. Anyway, it's been sort of rough since then. Elena's institutionalized."

"I know, Sam, and, again, I just have to tell you how sorry I am. I know it costs a bundle, always does. I'm not saying this to convince you, it's up to you, but we could take care of her maintenance, I'd insist on that as a part of your contract."

"Hap, let's leave out my personal problems. That's not why I came down here."

"Agreed—I was just trying to . . . hell, you understand . . . "

Linkum nodded.

"But what you should know is that I could be an embarrassment to you, Hap. You've got a career. Mine has just been shortstopped. Everybody's got bosses, yours would be shocked to know how I really feel about the chairborne commandos who set the policies in the White House and in State that killed Antonio. Besides being fuckers, I think they were war criminals. They should have been put in the dock, like the Nazis at Nuremberg. The country would have had an education—"

"What you're saying isn't new to me, Sam. You haven't exactly kept your ideas secret. You let them all hang out in print." He touched Linkum's file. "Even drawing the Vietnam-Nuremberg analogy. It's all here."

Linkum smiled, "I don't know whether I should be pleased or pissed that you've followed my stuff so closely."

"If you believed in what you wrote—pleased. Now, don't worry about embarrassing me. I don't know if you've tracked my career as closely as we've watched yours recently, but I run my own show as a civilian. Without sounding too damn immodest, I'll say they know they're lucky to have me in this spot. I could retire and quadruple my salary by working for one of the defense contractors. I turn them down regularly. I'm here not to feel the asses of the secretaries—that's just a fringe benefit at the Pentagon—but because of something else. I really *believe* in the necessity of the intelligence work we're doing because of what I know about how the hawks think—here and there. And, Sam, I have to tell you that I'm scared as hell. You will be, too, when I tell you why."

Hap Chorley checked his all-knowing chronometer. It was a precision intrument with separate dials that gave the time in both Washington and Moscow.

He punched the no-hands intercom to his secretary. "Maryjane, I'm leaving now but be sure to tell the duty officer that I'll stay in range within the District in case anything comes up. I'll be at home later on, exact time as yet unknown. I won't be needing my driver. Now you go home to your mother, honey, stay out of trouble, and I'll see you in the a. m."

Linkum followed him into the reserved parking lot. They got into his five-year-old Pontiac, which had no official markings. It was a familiar precaution: no conspicuous colors or license plates. Half-apologetically, Chorley said, "I keep my Bentley at the farm in Maryland. Come on, let's get us some fresh air." Chorley drove past the rows of crosses at the national cemetery and then across the Arlington Memorial Bridge. Suddenly, he slowed down and found a parking place near the Lincoln Memorial. They sat on a patch of greensward that faced the seated, brooding figure between the noble columns.

Chorley said:

"Here's the score, Sam. We're in a new ballgame. I'm not talking cold war to you. This is something that smells strange and altogether different to me. It's dangerous as hell—but, dammit, it's also a helluva chance for what I call peace by standoff."

Linkum frowned. "Hap, you're not going to lay on me that phony slogan—'Peace Is Our Profession'?"

"Jesus H. Christ, hear me out! I'm not here to con you, Sam. It's time for you to start catching up with what's been going on in the real world beyond—"

"Haven't you got it backwards? Is the real world our counter-intelligence against theirs, or our anti-missiles against their missiles?" He pointed toward the Lincoln Memorial. "That gloomy fellow up there once used a word during the Civil War that's stuck with me: *disenthrall*. Or, as we might put it more crudely, let's not bullshit ourselves. I think the Pentagon people are enthralled by the fun-and-games of continuing war by other means. And the defense budget is still that great big PX in the sky, with not much left over for the groundlings."

Chorley said, "I'm not going to argue with you, old cock, because—and don't let this shock you too much— I agree with maybe half the things you've just said. In my own way, I'm a maverick at the Pentagon myself—a loyal opposition maverick. I'm a civilian, I don't have to be there and they know it, and I'm not all that enthralled. But I know a few things that you don't know. You give me credit for those, and I'll concede in a second that I don't know a bloody thing about newspapers, your line of work. If after you hear what I have in mind you still feel the same way, no sweat, I'll put you on the next shuttle to LaGuardia."

"Okay, hit me," Linkum said. "I've made my speech for the day."

"And here's mine. This part you know: what you call the real world out there could be obliterated in twenty-four hours. We've got the kill and the overkill, and so have the Soviets. That's not news. But let's take it from there. I'm saying this: unless the top-level people in Washington and Moscow working in Intelligence can come to some sort of understanding to cool it, we're really done for. We're the ones who can dampen the fire. We're a third force, and we're the only ones who can bring the policymakers and militarists to their senses. I think I know how to give it a college try with the help of one man. *You.*"

"Hap, now I know you're off your rocker. *Me?*"

"*You,* yes, as the centerpiece of an operation that I'll explain in a moment. Let me give you a fast briefing on the current state of the art of Mutual Assured Destruction—MAD. We've gone from the era of the Big Bang boys—John Foster Dulles, Herman Kahn, Henry Kissinger—with their massive retaliation if the world didn't behave itself by their rules, to a more flexible posture of conventional arms and limited nuclear response. If they cross the firebreak, we come back with strikes against military targets only. The neutron warheads are fairly clean, killing by radiation instead of blast and heat. One of our neutron warheads can put out about ten thousand units of radiation. That's enough to take out anyone or anything around a primary target because any dosage over seven hundred rads is fatal. There could, of course, be some secondary radiation picked up by particles of dust that could possibly cause some problems with civilians—"

Linkum interrupted. "I was wondering when you'd get around to mentioning people. How does the new stuff compare to the Hiroshima and Nagasaki bombs or the calling-cards left by the B-52's in Vietnam?"

"Child's play. The first atomic toys were unsophisticated and the conventional tonnage in the Nam was uncontrollable. Now our delivery systems are better—a nice family of ground, sea, air and air-to-air missiles with multiple warheads and dial-a-yield destructiveness. But everything I've told you about our armor is pretty visible —and the same goes for theirs. Up to now."

Chorley looked around him, as if he was worried that someone could pick up his words or read his lips. Linkum asked him if he was wired and recording their conversation; Chorley told him that he wouldn't with a friend; Linkum said he believed him.

"This is your assignment, Sam: I want you to obtain a piece of information from the KGB—and to give them a piece of information."

Linkum grinned. "Is *that* all? I thought it was something tough. What do you want me to do—storm the Kremlin and steal it or just ask for it politely?"

"You dumb bastard, you're not as far off as you think you are. If we play our cards right, it might be ours for the asking."

"You know that I've never been very good at bluffing. Poker is your game."

Chorley thought for a moment. "The game would be more like bridge when nobody has enough cards to bid and the players decide to throw in their hands. In other words, the Russians are in the same spot that we're in—a game where neither of us can win."

"Well, it sounds better than that other game they invented—Russian roulette. All it takes is one in the chamber plus a little too much vodka and—"

"And that's one of the things we have to count on when we deal with their people on the decision-making level—that their instinct for self-preservation is just as strong as ours. And it is, if I've read their history of military adventurism rightly. Still, I'm not depending on their history or their goodwill to save their asses or ours. What we have to let them know is that we're both in a no-win situation. What I'm worried about is that some of their hotheads, given new scientific toys, might believe otherwise."

Linkum said, "And I'm supposed to make them cool it by obtaining one piece of paper? I don't get it, Hap."

"You will. Because to get a piece of paper, we, or rather *you*, have to give them a piece of paper. It's a tradeoff. The KGB, in the person of my opposite number, has to be convinced that the name of the game is show-and-tell."

"Now you're talking about two pieces of paper, and I'm still lost in the clouds."

"I can assure you that what you would be doing is very much down-to-earth," Chorley said. "As I used to tell you when I was taking your money in poker, once in a while it pays to show your opponent your hole card. Don't be afraid of the truth if you're able to cover your bluff with an ace in the hole."

Linkum said, "Okay, let's cut out the card games and parables. Are you allowed to tell me what's on their piece of paper and what's on ours?"

Chorley replied, "Not really. Not unless you actually undertake the assignment. I don't think you'd want to know, and carry the burden of knowing."

They circled around each other like boxers, feinting for weaknesses and looking for openings.

"But what I want you to do goes beyond pieces of paper, Sam. Because I know and you know that we're not going to be giving out any formulas to them, or they to us. What I'm trying to do is establish my good faith with them. The formality of putting something in writing shows that I'm dead serious because, dammit, I am. Things have gone too far to be anything but. I want to deal on a personal level so they'll know I'm acting in good faith. You're my emissary—that has to be made clear. It'll probably mean that you'll have to go to Moscow in the long run and speak to them directly—right to the top, if you can and they're willing to play—as if you're me. Even a negative answer can convey a message to me. There may have to be a few way-stops along the road but, if I know my opposite number, you'll get there."

Linkum rubbed his hand over his mouth and chin nervously, and stared toward the Memorial. Chorley watched him, waiting. Minutes passed. Then Linkum said:

"Before I say yes or no, I want to ask a question that may surprise you: Will I be in personal danger?"

Now it was Chorley's turn to hesitate.

"In the normal course of things, no."

"You don't sound very convinced. I'm not asking for a guarantee in writing but I'd like to have your real judgment, not an official one."

"That's why I chose my words carefully," Chorley said. "Under my plan of action, there's little chance of trouble for you personally. But once an operation gets rolling there can always be some human slipup—as you know. We've been through enough of them ourselves."

"Sure . . . Hap, it's different for me today. You

never married. I've got an invalid wife. And I don't know if you know this but there's another woman I'm close to. We love each other. You said that USAFSS would take care of Elena financially and that I appreciate, but this other woman is a part of my mixed-up life, a very big part, and I'm part of hers, too."

Linkum hesitated, waiting to see if Chorley knew about Jennie. But if his A-2 file included her, Chorley did not or maybe would not say.

"I'm not looking to be a hero," Linkum went on, "and I'm not exactly a patriot by your lights. But I have to admit that one thing you said gets to me—the chance to be in on an operation that could lead to at least a temporary peace by standoff—although I'm still not convinced you've got the right guy—"

"If you knew the details, you'd know why I think that you're not only the right guy but the *one* guy who could pull it off," Chorley said.

"Can you tell me this?" Linkum said. "Why can't something this big be handled by one of the professional CIA spooks instead of an old retread who's been off the firing line for so long and, besides has so many doubts—"

"Because, dammit, the CIA is not the big time! They're good for newspaper exposés and planted stories and books and winning Pulitzers for newspapermen who've been fed their line of crap by PR-types inside the company. In a way, I'm glad that even a smart guy like you is under the impression that the CIA is the primary intelligence agency. I can tell you that they're small potatoes compared to us."

"Who's us?"

"NSA, the National Security Agency, inside the Pentagon itself. We have the real resources. We don't go around shooting off our mouths. But we own the works —the cryptology, the international monitoring of all the military and civilian messages and signals, the counter-intelligence operations. Let Congress and the public think that the CIA runs the show. Let them have the credit—that's all to the good for us. But NSA has the manpower and the money. We're *operational*."

Linkum laughed. "Nothing will stop the Army Air Corps stuff—they're still playing your song."

"Damn right," Chorley said, elbowing him playfully. "And, as you might have guessed, USAFSS is more powerful than the Army or Navy intelligence branches inside NSA. I happen to be the only civilian director. They're stuck with the brass and braid."

"Okay—I'm impressed."

"Sam, if I hear you right, there's just one thing you'd like to button up. Your lady friend. What did you say her name was?"

"I didn't say."

Chorley put on his boyish expression.

"But if you want to know, I'll tell you. It's no secret, let alone top secret. Her name is Jennie Ives, she's a helluva good journalist, and she's on the network's cut list—due to be fired in the next few days for so-called economy reasons. If I undertook your assignment, I'd probably wind up in one place—no, don't tell me where —she'd be somewhere else looking for another newspaper job, and there wouldn't be anyone around to look in on Elena once in a while—"

Chorley interrupted him with a snapping of his fingers, signaling his next brainstorm.

"Would your friend want to stay put in her job if she could?" Linkum nodded. "Well, then, who the fuck is her boss?" Linkum mentioned Jane Twining Delafield, and explained that the newspaper now came under her as vice president in charge of the leisure-time division.

"As far as I'm concerned, she's dirt," Chorley said. "And she's got bosses, too—the people I deal with."

"Are you serious? Delafield is pretty high up there and, besides, she's got three testicles under her skirt."

"Well, hers can be cut, too. What if I told you right here and now that Jennie's job is absolutely safe, that nobody else's will be taken away because of her, and that if necessary she may even have to join you—like to cover something you're up to? Would that make a difference to you?"

"Come on, Hap, you mean to say that USAFSS can tell the network who to hire—"

"It's been known to happen. At all three networks. In the interests of national security—you've heard that phrase before, haven't you? I'm telling you, she won't be fired, no matter which way you decide. As a favor for an old friend." He paused. "Of course, she doesn't have to know how."

"You guys can really flex your muscles, can't you? The funny thing is, I believe you can do it."

"No sweat, old buddy. Now think of yourself. You're on the beach. You've got financial burdens. The

76

assignment won't take long—it could be a week or a
month or two, depending. Under the personal contract
I'll write for you, which no one will know about except
your coded A-2 file and me, you'll be paid as a consultant
for two years."

Chorley looked at him for a reaction. "It's not just
the dough, Sam, or I wouldn't be sitting here with you
or anyone else. I'm asking you to do it because, as you'll
see in a moment, I hope, you're the one American who
can carry it off. And another thing: it's an honorable
assignment."

Chorley untangled his legs from the spongy grass
and brushed himself off. He extended his hand to Linkum. Both men stood facing each other, waiting. Then
Linkum grasped Chorley's hand, shaking it hard once.

"Hap, you're a fucker," he said, a smile creeping up
the corners of his mouth, his face still rigid in the jaws.

"You won't regret it, old cock," Chorley said, more
pleased than triumphant.

"Do you really think so?" Linkum murmured, more
to himself.

They walked to Chorley's parked car. He looked
under the hood, then removed a piece of thread before
opening the doors. Instinctively, both men glanced in
passing toward the Lincoln Memorial. To avoid the District traffic in the late afternoon, Chorley drove alongside the Potomac, crossed the Chain Bridge into
Virginia, then recrossed farther west and picked up the
River Road toward his farm in Maryland.

All through dinner they reminisced about the war
years when they had been together, and caught up on the

fleeting years afterward, when conquests and glories had shrunk to such small measure.

"Sam, the Russkies have a plan to hit us—somewhere and soon—*geologically*," Chorley said. "It's a brilliant notion for a simple reason: it would be almost impossible for us to know—or to publicly admit—that they were the cause. Frankly, I'm scared shitless."

The USAFSS director opened up a bottle of Jack Daniel's, poured the sour mash neat in waterglasses, and lit their Havanas.

"What I want you to do," he went on, "is to assess their capability, to let them know that *we* know what they're planning, and to get from *them* the piece of paper giving the time, place and details."

"Is that all?" Linkum said. "I thought it was going to be something tough."

"I don't blame you for thinking I'm a little nuts. But this isn't a caper with dead drops, plastic charges, microdot communications and an L-pill under your tongue in case you're caught redhanded. Strange as it may sound, you'll only succeed with *their* cooperation. I'm not changing my story, but there's an easy way and a hard way to pull it off. The easy way is to get them to play ball —to see it our way. The hard way would be a little more complicated, and risky. It would mean turning one of their people."

"Well, I always heard there were no free lunches."

"You may know him. Do you recall a fellow we used to do business with when we were tracking down the paintings that the Nazis stole in Italy and shipped back to Germany? In those rosy days when the Russians were trading cases of vodka for Mickey Mouse watches and even sharing intelligence? Andrei Glazunov."

"Andrei? The art expert from the Hermitage who was always quoting Russian peasant proverbs?"

"The same. He's gone up in the world. Doing some free lance work for the GRU—their military intelligence that parallels ours—plus, if my information is correct, for the Fifth Directorate of the KGB."

"But he really knows his stuff—I've read catalogues he's written on Renaissance art. He's a helluva guy in the field. And he was one of the more reasonable people we ran into."

"I'm glad you think so, Sam, because you're going to be meeting him again in a few days. Be sure to wear the ribbon from your old Order of Suvorov that the Russians gave us. It might be a nice, warming touch. After all, we *were* on the same side once."

Four

WHEN THE ALITALIA flight from Rome landed that morning with a screeching of brakes but without mishap near the end of the runway at Punta Raisi airdrome, perilously close to the gulf along the nacreous Tyrrhenian Sea, the Sicilian businessmen in pin-striped dark double-breasted suits as well as the homecoming contract laborers in patched muscle-bulging jackets applauded the pilot and the other moustaches in the cockpit. They crossed themselves and offered a thankful prayer to Palermo's own ravished patron, Saint Rosalia, who several centuries before had stopped the slaughter of a dreadful plague, for still another miracle.

Sam Linkum descended the rolled-up steps, fended off two rival porters who attempted to seize his luggage and Olivetti typewriter, and offered his own silent resolve: *I will avoid airlines where pilots are applauded for making a safe landing, I will avoid airlines where hostesses balance themselves in open-toed high heels, I will avoid airlines where the*

theme from The Godfather *is played like the national anthem.*
And he added to himself: Don't let the heat get you, this
is only the start; keep cool.

The cloying sirocco enveloped him immediately; it
was redolent of garlic, sulphurous hardboiled eggs, and
peperoni arrosta. The self-important cement and highway
contractors, picked up by bowing company chauffeurs
opening doors of Mercedes-Benz limousines with jump
seats, looked with patronizing smiles at the peasant fare
thrust upon fathers and sons by sobbing, shouting wives
and mothers in conventional mourning dress. The
women had not seen their menfolk for a month but wel-
comed them home, first with food and then with chesty
embraces, as if they had returned like conquering, bread-
winning *condottieri* from a strange and pillaged foreign
country, which mainland Italy's northern factory cities
were compared to Sicily's parochial towns and shuttered
villages of suspicion and respect.

"Welcome to Palermo, Mr. Linkum," a voice behind
him said. "Can I give you a lift to your hotel?"

The voice belonged to an American. Midwest, nasal.
Linkum turned around.

"Dan McDavitt, from the embassy in Rome, on a
short looksee here." He appeared to be in his early thirties, florid, with a slight paunch.

"I didn't expect a welcoming committee," Linkum
said.

"No committee—just a party of one," McDavitt replied, affably. "Here, let me give you a hand with your
stuff before the pirates get it."

He took Linkum's one suitcase and dropped it in the

back of the Alfa-Romeo with diplomatic license plates. They drove along the coastal road in the direction of Mondello Lido, and far in the distance Linkum finally recognized an old landmark, the crouching dog-shaped Capo Gallo on the far side of the bay.

Linkum listened to the small talk and then enquired, "Do all Americans get this kind of personal service?"

"Only a few." McDavitt laughed. "You're with the big network in New York, aren't you? I was coming out here, anyway, and I thought—"

"No, I'm not with the network, thank you." McDavitt looked puzzled. "Well, I guess you might say they were my employers, temporarily, pro tem, briefly, so your intelligence is just a bit behind the times. I'm just a free lance, with a small art publication."

"No problem," McDavitt said casually. "Glad to be of assistance. You're here to cover the big Russian propaganda show at the National Gallery tomorrow, aren't you?"

"I heard that something was cooking there," Linkum replied with equal matter-of-factness. "Do you think it's worth a visit?"

McDavitt laughed. "Depends if you're a Madonna freak or not," he said. "I got a bellyful from the Sisters back in Akron so I go in for the more modern stuff myself. You seen one Crucifixion, you seen them all." He put his hand on Linkum's sleeve. "No offense intended if you're devout."

When they reached the turnoff toward Punta Acquasanta, McDavitt said, "I suppose you're staying at the Villa Igiea?"

"Too rich for my blood—and too far out of the center of the city," Linkum said. "I've got a reservation at the Palme on the Via Roma. But I don't want to take you out of your way. You can drop me off anywhere along here and I can grab a taxi. If I remember correctly, it isn't more than a few miles to town."

"You know Palermo?"

"I used to work this beat a hundred years ago," Linkum said. "With Garibaldi's Thousand or Patton's Seventh Army, it's so long ago I forget which."

"No trouble at all. I'm going right past the Palme. If we run into each other again, I'd very much like to hear about those days." McDavitt grinned boyishly. "That's a funny line you've got about Garibaldi and Patton—did you actually ever see the old boy in person? I saw the movie they made about his life. Terrific."

"I caught his act once or twice, right here in Palermo, between beachheads. Pearl-handled or rather ivory-handled revolvers, slung low like a gunfighter, lots of stars all over him—they used to swear that he had them sewn on his pajamas—but the funny thing was that when he opened his mouth, in spite of the whole mystique around him of the fighting dismounted cavalryman, out came a high, squeaky voice, not at all like George C. Scott's."

"Well, I'll be darned," said McDavitt.

Suddenly he swung his car ahead of a doubleparked Fiat and muttered in less Boy Scout fashion, "Sicilian bastard," and in return got the double horns from the driver's fingers.

Linkum said, "Do you mind slowing down a bit? I'm still adjusting to the time and the traffic."

"Probably one of those Red bastards. He must have noticed the diplomatic plates. Once these people get behind the wheel of one of their pissassed little Fiats, they all get political. I call them Commiekazes."

McDavitt's Alfa-Romeo pulled up in front of the Palme's faded grandeur and doubleparked. He blew his horn to summon the hall porter.

"Well, here we are—made it again safely," McDavitt said, grinning broadly. "It was an unexpected pleasure—a real great honor to see and hear you, sir."

"Thanks for the lift," Linkum said. Whenever anyone called him "sir," he felt uncomfortable—either old or patronized.

"Maybe we'll run into each other sometime soon—"

"I suspect we will," Linkum said.

McDavitt offered his hand; his hard grip whitened Linkum's knuckles.

Linkum noticed the ring he was wearing—the ram's horns encircling the elevated green glass stone.

It was a dead giveaway: Fordham University, the favorite recruiting campus after Notre Dame for agents of the FBI and CIA.

At half-past five the next morning, Sam Linkum heard the rumbling of Sherman tanks. He thought he was dreaming. The rolling thunder and clanking on the cobblestones continued after he opened his eyes. Standing to one side, he threw open the fixed shutters and peered through the decorative grillwork on the false balcony to the street below. Along the length of the Via Roma, legions of trucks battled for position and prestige: the new Shermans of agriculture and dusty industry, carrying produce and contraband under roped-up tarpaulins. Everything appeared to be sound language and secretive signs that no outsider could comprehend in the afterdawn of Sicily.

He awoke with the city; it was too late to try catching up on his sleep again. The ceremony where he planned to observe Andrei Glazunov was set for ten o'clock at the Palazzo Abatellis. Linkum knew that his human target—his former comrade-in-arms-and-art— was already in Palermo. For a mile off the apron at Punta Raisi, guarded by a ring of military police in Snow White helmets, he had spotted the high-winged tail and four jet pods of an Aeroflot IL-62M. The yellow hammer and sickle emblazoned on the bright red flag painted on the Soviet airliner's tail flew here far less frequently than the Stars and Stripes. The Russians usually plied these monitored waters under the Mediterranean.

Walking through the lobby of the striving but not-quite grand hotel, Linkum marveled at the statuary; sensuous nineteenth-century nudes without nipples or pubic hair carrying functional water pitchers with sweet innocence—early *Playboy* bunnies. Along the strada he sipped his cup of coffee with the clerks and cleanup men at the standup bar. The aroma of the espresso and of the night's rinds blended in the noisome air. Palermo appealed to all his senses again.

He thought of scouting the Palazzo before the guests

turned up but then changed his mind: better to observe in a crowded place than to be observed as an American. Strangers could always tell outsiders. It had something to do with your haircut and shoes: unlike weapons, they could not be concealed. No one who was anyone would arrive for at least a couple of hours. Even at art galleries and museums, officials required grand entrances. With some time to kill, Linkum unfolded the pocket map of Palermo's unchanged streets and began to stroll along the waterfront. The flaked stone palaces and tenement warrens crisscrossed with flags of laundry broke down class distinctions between the titled and impoverished. The old city was still a mixture of baroque and bombed.

Linkum entered the public gardens of the Villa Giulia on Via Lincoln and sat alone on a half-broken bench beneath bougainvillea vines. No one was around. He studied the photograph of Andrei Glazunov that Hap Chorley had given him. But he knew it wouldn't be necessary once the ceremony started, and being seen with the photograph might prove to be an embarrassment. All those "Commiekazes" had to be sprinkled in the audience; this day belonged to the Russians. Lighting a cigarette as if a nonexistent wind would blow out the match, with the same motion he cupped the photograph in the curled palm of his hand and burned it into ashes.

When he entered the courtyard of the Palazzo Abatellis that had been converted into the National Gallery of Sicily, a few hundred people were already there. A busload of German tourists streamed out of the rooms and through the stone portals and monopolized the folding chairs placed there for the ceremony. Linkum slipped into the half-empty row behind them. He overheard their tour guide explain in a guttural Bavarian accent that the Palazzo had been severely damaged by American Flying Fortresses. For a moment, he wished he could step out of his role and say: Up yours, *mein herr*, our aim was maybe a little off but we intended no harm at the time, what we wanted to do was clobber you civilized gentlemen.

The immorality of Vietnam that had caused Antonio's death had so overtaken his mind and altered his life and ruined Elena's, he was surprised to discover that he could still be aroused by his old war's forgotten enemy. Outside on the Via Alloro, he heard a roar of raced motors, followed by a slamming of doors. A procession of Palermitani adorned in the black and gold-chained splendor appropriate for funerals and stately occasions escorted the Soviet delegation to the elevated courtyard platform. Linkum immediately spotted Andrei Glazunov. The twinkle was still in his eyes and the laugh lines had creased his face even more deeply. He was the only personage who did not appear solemn. And there were the hair and shoes again: he wore his longer than his Soviet colleagues and his Italian loafers contrasted with the thick rubber soles of the security officers around him. How much of it was a pose? The front row of chairs was cordoned off for the diplomatic corps from Rome and dignitaries from the university and museum world; only the purple from the Palermo cathedral was absent—the cardinal did not lend his presence to the forces of the anti-Christ from the godless lands beyond the Bosporus.

"My dear friends," Glazunov said, speaking in Italian. "You know why I am here. I do not have to make a flowery speech nor even a long one—have no fear. We have a saying in my country among the peasants: If you're a rooster, crow, if you're a hen, lay eggs. This morning, before the eyes of the artists and scholars who know so much more than do I, you will not hear me crow." He pointed to the easel next to him that was covered with a velvet cloth. "Everything I could possibly say can be said better by looking at the painting that I am about to unveil. In my humble opinion, as curator of the Department of Western European Art at the Hermitage in Leningrad, it is one of the greatest paintings of the fifteenth century. We have in my department various religious objects and relics, including coins of the conquerors of Sicily, the Normans, which I invite all present here to see some day in my city. But I would not compare any of these to this beautiful painting—Antonello da Messina's *Annunciation*."

Glazunov smiled and nodded to the Italian curator at his side from the National Gallery. He lifted the velvet covering. The onlookers gasped. Linkum had seen some reproductions before of Antonello's *L'Annunziata* in prewar art books; but none had captured the painting's inner vision or caught the subtle expression on the young woman's face. For the Madonna appeared to be at a suspended moment in time, herself surprised, looking up intelligently from a book and reading stand, her features exquisitely composed, her face radiant and bathed in the beauty of life, the sensual flesh tones contrasting brightly against a rich sea-blue mantle, enfolded modestly over her bosom by the delicate fingers of her left hand, and only the upraised fingers of her right hand suggesting the wondrous, spiritual instant of incarnation.

A voice behind him broke the spell.

"If you get your kicks from Madonnas, that one's good for at least three Poseidon nuclear subs."

McDavitt, as expected, had turned up—but was he there to observe Glazunov, or him?, Linkum wondered.

"In propaganda value alone," McDavitt went on, "the Reds are having a ball here. Probably be good for a couple of seats in the Sicilian regional parliament. What the hell, you win some, you lose some—today belongs to the Comrades."

His voice was loud enough to be heard by the tourists in the row ahead. They motioned him to be still, as if staring down a loudmouth in a movie house. Glazunov was speaking again.

Linkum quickly turned around and whispered, "How come Washington sends knuckleheads like you overseas?"

McDavitt looked surprised, and then grinned weakly.

" . . . rightfully belongs here in the National Gallery where we are honored to stand," Glazunov continued. "Antonello may be considered a member of the Venetian School, but the sunlight in his painting originated in his native Sicily." The audience applauded. Like many other native sons, Antonello had run off as soon as possible and only the city of his birth in his name linked him to Sicily. "The provenance of this masterpiece you already know for it has been preserved for more than four centuries, but what happened later and why are we standing here at this moment in twentieth century history?"

Linkum wondered if Glazunov would really tell all the details—including why the painting had taken this long to be returned.

"I do not speak as a politician but as a museum curator, like my colleagues from Sicily and Italy. In the Great War for the liberation of all European peoples from the yoke of Nazism and Fascism, it was my great privilege to be assigned to a military unit concerned with the recovery of art works stolen by the Germans. I did not carry a gun, I carried my catalogues. The Hermann Goering Division, which occupied Sicily, had attached to it a number of experts from the Einsatzstab Rosenberg, the official looting organization. Their job was to steal works of art and bring them back for the private collections of Hitler and Goering. After all, did not Hitler himself say, 'We are barbarians and we wish to be barbarians—it is an honorable calling'?"

In the courtyard of Palazzo Abatellis, the German tourists stiffened in their seats but their faces registered no emotion. Glazunov must have been aware of their presence; they were the largest foreign group present and they sat together. His talk undoubtedly had been cleared by the KGB officer at the Soviet Embassy in Rome, but he made no effort to change the harsh language.

"And so the Goering Division's official art looters knew exactly what they were after in Palermo and elsewhere in Italy. They wanted Italian masters from the

Sienese to the Venetians. Above all, those of the fifteenth and sixteenth centuries—Bellini, Titian, Bordone and Antonello, this gem of the National Gallery. We discovered their orders: No pieces 'attributed to' or 'from the school of' but works by the masters themselves. In the Schloss Weesenstein, near the city of Dresden—which was captured by the glorious Red Army—my colleagues and I found the official card catalogue of the collections of the so-called Fuehrermuseum. This helped us to identify most of the valuable works and return them to their rightful countries. Of course, there were many claims and we did not want to make any mistakes. Some paintings are world treasures—surely not the property of private collectors or dealers to be sold to the highest bidders in the West. I can assure you that your *Annunciation* was most carefully guarded and preserved, under ideal conditions, at the Hermitage."

Glazunov placed a hand on the ornate frame and signaled the National Gallery curator to hold the other side for the benefit of the photographers. Then he added formally, "This Renaissance masterpiece by Antonello da Messina is hereby restored by the people of the Soviet Union to the people of the Italian Republic, now too under the leadership of the Communist Party."

The audience applauded Glazunov's carefully prepared remarks. The German tourists walked in a group, after counting heads, to their bus, and the dignitaries looked at their watches.

"Sorry if I offended, sir," McDavitt said, "but if anything was ever a show—"

"Forget it," Linkum said.

92

McDavitt filed out with the government officials, stopping to make some notes about those who attended, and then drove off in his Alfa-Romeo.

Linkum reached into his pocket and affixed the Order of Suvorov ribband to the notch in his lapel. He couldn't remember the last time he had worn it; and then he suddenly did: when he had been married in uniform and pieces of colored cloth for accidents of achievement and bravery still seemed important.

He followed Andrei Glazunov and the National Gallery curator as they walked under the loggia and then up the narrow stairway of Palazzo Abetellis to Hall X. The famous Antonello was hung prominently in the center of the room; the brilliance of the Madonna's mantle paled the dark, lacquered paintings nearby. The two curators drew back and studied the masterpiece from different angles. Linkum watched them and, for the first time, openly made a few reminder notes in his own shorthand of what he had seen and heard in the courtyard. He thought it might be wise to be observed here as simply another writer for another obscure art publication.

As the curators left Hall X and began to stroll toward the other rooms, Linkum made his move.

"Hello, Andrei," he said, speaking in Italian. "The Antonello is everything you said it is."

Glazunov nodded and replied matter-of-factly, "Yes, yes, truly beautiful."

Of course he had not recognized him; not after a generation and more of crooked turns on the roadways of their lives.

Then he added in English, deliberately, "If you're a rooster, crow, if you're a hen, lay eggs."

Glazunov now stared at him closely for the first time.

Then he suddenly said, "We've met before."

Instinctively, he glanced around the gallery: the look of a man who checked to see if he was being overheard before talking openly.

Glazunov's eyes lighted on the ribband in Linkum's lapel.

"Where did you get this, friend?" he continued in Italian.

"From you, Capitano," Linkum replied in English.

Glazunov peered at Linkum's features and a look of recognition crossed his face. He punched Linkum's chest and grasped his hand.

"Capitano Linkum!"

"Capitano Glazunov!"

They embraced, and Glazunov, speaking in English for the first time, said, "What in the world are you doing here, Sam?"

"Andrei, I came here to listen to a great Renaissance scholar and to see a great painting—for the second time."

"Sam," Glazunov said, poking him playfully, "there's an old peasant saying from America that you once taught me. It goes: You are full of horse manure."

"Where can we talk in private?"

Glazunov glanced around the room; in a corner of the gallery stood one of the close-cropped members of the Soviet delegation who had the look of security imprinted on his eyeballs.

"Private is difficult. Perhaps public is more private, especially if we speak in English. They," Glazunov said, motioning over his shoulder, "don't understand us. The ones who came along were picked because they studied Italian in school. Anyway, I'm here just for another day of ceremonies. Then home to Leningrad. We have our own aircraft which must keep a schedule—"

"I noticed your big Ilyushin parked out at Punta Raisi. You've come up in the world, old friend." He felt genuinely happy to see him, mission apart. "And your Italian is pretty remarkable. That was quite a speech you gave, even with its omissions."

"My field of study. I live in past centuries so I find myself getting to this part of the world every few years. But I haven't been south of Naples since our old days."

Glazunov checked his watch.

"But we have to get together alone, without these jokers around us. Jokers, right? Did I remember the right word?"

"Precisely, Andrei. I can't think of a better word to describe your friends eavesdropping on our conversation."

"Don't worry about them." He touched the Soviet decoration in Linkum's lapel. "This comes in handy on such occasions. Now, let's get down to the brass tacks. Brass pins? Tacks. I have this afternoon free until dinner time. Can you visit me after lunch at the Villa Igiea?"

"I was going to suggest the place where I'm staying, the Palme on the Via Roma, but neither one is very private."

"I remember the Grande Albergo e delle Palme,"

Glazunov said. "You put me up there once. The hotel that had—does it still have?—a lobby filled with marble titties."

"You weren't supposed to notice or remember. Not your period—nineteenth century. Nothing's changed, except the uniforms. But I have a better idea. Let's drive out to Segesta, where we can be alone, and see that remarkable temple sitting there in the valley."

"Magnificent! I can't leave the island without seeing Segesta. How shall we get there? Do you have tires? Wait a minute. Correction: Do you have *wheels*?"

Glazunov was pleased that his slang had come back.

Linkum said that he could rent a Fiat right at the hotel, but Glazunov said it would be a waste of good talking time to drive out separately.

"The curator from the National Gallery has provided me with his own chauffeur," Glazunov said. "I'll pick you up at exactly 1500 hours."

They turned off the state highway and circled the gorge in the valley below Mount Barbaro and, suddenly, in the cleft of the rocks and of time, they came upon the great unfinished Doric temple, toylike in the distance, standing bareboned under the sky, as it had stood for twenty-five centuries, its rough travertine glowing mauve in the late afternoon. The countryside brooded in a melancholy fertility, without a sign of human habitation; wild fennel from another season held the soil in withered rows and cactus flowered in surprising purple bursts under the dying light; and the tops of the feathery thistles were alive with butterflies; above the naked shell

96

and within the colonnade of pillars, sparrowhawks wheeled and screamed in pursuit of swiftly diving swallows that nested in the temple's entablature; and the winds captured in the valley raised swirls of crushed hornstone dust. The silence in the valley of Segesta was stunning: but in the far reaches of the imagination they could envision the tramping boots and chariots of the Elymians and Trojans and Carthaginians and, from their own time, the helmeted warriors and rumbling armor passing by the dead civilizations of Magna Graecia to liberate another bondaged island in the Mediterranean Sea.

After the chauffeur parked the Fiat sedan and entered the cafe and replica shop at the foot of the temple, Linkum and Glazunov walked the twisting roadway up toward the small Greek theatre that overlooked the valley and the Gulf of Castellammare. They planted themselves in seats hewn into the solid rock, staring at the bare, stubbled stage that played only to a company of lizards, and then raised their sights to the gently rising hills interrupting the horizon.

"What in the hell happened, Sam?"

They were alone at last, unobserved and unheard, for the first time since the wartime days when they were tracking down clues to the whereabouts of the plundered masterpieces.

"Do you want the sacred or the profane answer?"

"The truthful one, if possible."

"I'm afraid I'm not smart enough to figure out the truthful one, Andrei. So I'll tell you the answer in my own dumb way: I think we were screwed by history."

"That's close enough to the truth, Sam. I wish I had the answer to my own question but I wanted to hear it from you."

"I'm sorry that I didn't put it to you first." Linkum smiled, reached for a pebble, and tossed it at a lizard. "You usually had the appropriate Russian proverb to explain serious matters. You've failed me, friend."

"Oh, I could come up with something, if you wish, even if you like to kid me. The peasants used to say: The greatest Tsar must be put to bed with a shovel at last. We had our Tsar after the war—Stalin. Of course, he was a useful tyrant when we were fighting the Nazis, a great wartime leader, like your Roosevelt. But there was too much blood on his hands. The Soviet people lived with fear instead of a free Socialist system—and fear became the Fifth Horseman in relations between our two countries."

"We can sit here and talk about such things now because of our own private pasts," Linkum replied. "It was not all one-sided. We may not have had tyrants but we had some fools and small men in the White House who made the dream dissolve."

"The dream, Sam, the naive dream that after our war it would be different."

"Let's live with those dreams. Otherwise, we'll forget that there was a chance and still may be. We had some genuine killers in business suits, respectable foreign policy leaders who saw every uprising against the old ways as a Red plot. They left a heritage of fear that eventually led to the disaster in Vietnam—the most anti-American war conducted by Americans in this century.

And I don't forget that the same stupidity infected my country from within and gave a hunting license to the McCarthys and Nixons—oh, we had some prize bastards and only the shovel could put them to bed."

Glazunov said, "That isn't a bad proverb at all—I lend it to you without interest payments, Sam. It covers a variety of sins and sinners."

The Soviet curator reached into his rucksack and took out a powerful hand telescope. "Very useful for looking at brush strokes in a painting." He stood up on the stone seat of the theatre and gazed at the temple far below. "We're not the only ones interested in Segesta, I notice," he said. Two more cars were parked outside the cafe, not far from theirs. "My people are a little obvious and overprotective." He shrugged, and passed the telescope to Linkum. The American stood up on the stone seat and refocused the outer lens. The third car appeared to be an Alfa-Romeo; but it was parked sideways and he was not able to see if it had a diplomatic license plate.

"One of your people?" Glazunov asked, and Linkum replied, "I wouldn't be at all surprised."

"Our security people from Aeroflot are very interested in Hellenistic temples," Glazunov said, not hiding the sarcasm.

"And ours in American journalists who sit with Russian curators," Linkum said. "If it's who I think it is, he should get along very well with your gumshoes—a natural affinity there."

"Gumshoes? That's one I never heard of."

"I'll have to send you some detective stories so you can polish your American slang. We're both being followed—tailed. They're keeping an eye on us to make sure that we don't fall off the mountain."

Glazunov collapsed the telescope and put it back in his rucksack. Fury colored his cheeks.

"Those gumshoes better not try to tail us here. They're not the only ones who know influential officials in Moscow. Sam, don't judge us by those animals."

"I'm not a judge, Andrei. I don't think they'll dare to be that obvious, anyway. At least the American won't —I told him he was a loudmouth fool this morning when you were making your presentation at the National Gallery."

Linkum listened carefully and reminded himself of his mission: Glazunov's anger was a hopeful sign.

"Well, I want you to know that I'm here as an art curator and nothing else. Now, let's forget those people and catch up with ourselves. Since we've already solved the world's problems, let's turn to our own. What kind of work have you been doing? Have you got family? Why, if I may ask, are you in Palermo? It isn't just to hear me make a speech and see the Antonello, correct?"

"As usual, capitano, you're a man who gets to the point quickly. That hasn't changed. And I'll get to what I have to say almost as soon. There is something important that I have on my mind—"

"Capitano, I have something on my mind that is *not* important, but I wish to say it first. You asked me a question after we met at Palazzo Abatellis which—as you know—I did not answer. Right then and there, I was not able to give proper credit to the role you and your colleague, the fat major, played in tracking down the Antonello and some of the other masterpieces that were stolen by the Hermann Goering Division. What was that major's name again?"

"Hap Chorley."

"Yes, Major Hap Chorley, the jolly fellow who smoked the smelly cigars. He's still alive?"

"I believe he is," Linkum said. "I heard that he retired some time ago. As a brigadier general."

"What you must realize is that I did include our Soviet-American teamwork in the speech that I originally wrote in Leningrad. But it had to be approved by two different agencies in Moscow. When it was returned to me—*kaput*. Your Art Looting Investigation Unit had been killed. And with those gumshoes around I could not put my original words back into the speech. Sitting here in Segesta, together as friends, this I had to tell you. I am sorry—I apologize."

"I suspected as much, Andrei. But it's important for me to hear you say it."

"Well, I am sure that the Sicilian museum personnel know the true facts. They're the ones who count with me, not the Party functionaries."

"Do you mean the Russian or Italian Communists?"

Glazunov laughed. "My country's of course. "Ever since the Italian CP took over the Rome Government, Moscow has been unhappy with them. The Italian Communists have the crazy idea that their first loyalty is to Italy."

Linkum again found himself encouraged by Glazunov's candor, and humor about his candor.

"But why in the hell did it take so long for this

Antonello to be returned, Andrei? You and I know it belonged in Palazzo Abatellis."

"It would have taken longer if some of us had not pushed the Ministry of Culture, year after year. I don't have any illusions about the bureaucrats in any country. There's an old saying in the Ukraine: You can pull and pull, but you can't milk a bull. What surely caused them to change their minds was the change in the Italian Government."

The automobiles were still parked below the temple; but no one had started up the roadway leading to where they sat in the ancient Greek theatre.

"I still remember how you came here as a liaison officer, Andrei, and helped my unit by identifying some of the looted art."

"I'll never forget it, Sam—it was our personal meeting at the Elbe, with catalogues instead of carbines. That part of my speech, at least, remained."

They talked of the time that Hitler, Goering and Bormann had competed for the artistic wealth of Occupied Europe—including the private collections of the Rothschilds and other Jews with rare paintings, sculpture, books, and coins. Masterpieces from Sicily and Italy were taken for "safekeeping," all duly noted and receipted with proper Germanic efficiency. The trains carrying Jews to concentration camps beyond the Alps also carried stolen art. Paintings from Monte Cassino Abbey and other sacred places caught in the crossfire of war never arrived in the vaults of the Vatican. The Einsatzstab Rosenberg had done its work well for the Third Reich's greater glory; Hitler had planned to establish a cultural capital of the New Europe in his home city of Linz. Much of the plunder was discovered in a salt mine in the remote village of Alt Aussee in Austria. Then, in the dying springtime of war, the race was on between the Soviet and American armies to capture territory and with it to gain political domination of new governments. Sam Linkum was detached from an intelligence operation with the partisans in the Po Valley and sent to Austria to work with the MFA&A—the Monuments, Fine Arts, and Archives Section of Allied Supreme Headquarters. In Austria, he met Andrei Glazunov for the first time and they hit it off immediately. Glazunov had arrived in the American sector to help MFA&A identify the paintings and their provenance. Although he was not allowed to bring along the official card catalogue from the Schloss Weesenstein that had been taken by the Red Army, he carried a great deal of information in his head. Together, the Soviet and American captains retraced the origins of many of the major Renaissance works back to Sicily and Italy. This was the flowering of Linkum's interest in art—and the beginning of his long-nurtured hope that, even with the differences, it would be possible to live in some harmony with the Russians.

Linkum wondered, "Have you been at the Hermitage all this time?" And Glazunov replied, "Yes, happily so, because while the positions of the leaders in the Politburo change every May Day, my paintings—from Titian to Matisse to a few Americans like Rockwell Kent—are neither promoted nor downgraded."

"Andrei, I have something important that I want to speak to you about. Let me first answer your questions and catch you up quickly. Maybe I should have been a curator, too, living in a pleasant century, but instead I picked the twentieth and became a journalist. No, I did not come here just to hear you speak, but I am doing a little article about the return of the Antonello for an art magazine. Since you asked, my wife and I had one child —a son—and he was killed in Vietnam."

Glazunov put his arms around Linkum sympathetically. "The saying goes, the old warriors live, the sons die needlessly. If it is any consolation, he left a worse world than ours. Permit me to say as an official atheist: God rest his soul. I am very sorry to hear of this, Sam."

"Thank you, Andrei. and your family?"

"My two daughters left the nest a few years ago— one is married, the other a perpetual graduate student at the university. My wife and I are alone in a three-room apartment."

"You're happy?"

"Life goes on."

They watched the sun cast an orange glow over the Gulf of Castellammare beyond the temple and interrupting hills of Segesta. A great peace enveloped the valley.

"Andrei, I'm here in Palermo on a mission—to see you."

Glazunov nodded.

"Are you in the reserve? CIA?"

"No—to both questions. Especially not CIA."

"I am still in the reserve—one never leaves Intelligence in my country."

"I know that—that's why I came to speak to you."

"Sam, I'm listening, but with my guard up."

"Fair enough. I'm not asking you to trust me. I'm not asking you for a favor. I'm asking you—"

"How did you know that I'm still connected with military intelligence?"

"From *our* military intelligence."

"You're with the Army Security Agency—ASA?"

"No, but I see that you're pretty well-informed yourself. I'm not in the military at all, not even remotely connected. But I'm doing a job for Hap Chorley."

"Well, well—I thought you told me he was retired. Which story should I believe?"

For the first time there was an edge in his voice.

"Andrei, that wasn't a lie—I just kept back the details. Frankly, I had to know if your current views matched mine on the state of affairs between our two countries. If all the hatred and rhetoric had changed things between us. I'm willing to take a chance—on you, and on myself."

"But what has Hap Chorley got to do with us?"

"He's now a civilian who works at the Pentagon as head of Air Force intelligence operations. If you're interested, both his girth and his cigars have grown. But your intelligence services probably know more about his career than I do. Perhaps you do, yourself—"

"Sam, I told you, I'm a curator, not a KGB agent."

"And I'm a journalist—or, at least, *was* one—not a CIA agent."

"What do you mean, *was?*"

"Until a few weeks ago I worked for a newspaper, but then it was conglomeratized—taken over by one of the big corporations that run television. I had the funny notion that newspapers should print news. Anyway, making a long story short, I'm now, as we say, on the street."

"When money speaks, truth keeps its mouth shut— you know that proverb, Sam?"

"It sounds American enough to me."

"A Russian export."

"I guess it covers the situation."

"And now you're working for Hap Chorley again?"

"Yes—on one last informal mission that, I hope, can cool things down. I hope you'll think so too."

"And *I* hope you realize that you are talking to a very unimportant person. What can I do?"

"You're listening to an equally unimportant person. Maybe that's what could be most useful—you and I can speak on a human level."

"We are doing that right now. But as you noticed at the National Gallery, I have many bosses over me."

"Andrei, here's why I'm here and what it's all about: the Pentagon wants the GRU to know that Air Force intelligence—and I don't mean the CIA—is aware of a Soviet intelligence plan to strike somewhere *geologically*. To hit us at some weak point in one of the earth faults in the United States. Have you heard about it?"

"That is incredible! Doubly so: that it would occur or that I would be told about it."

"Exactly how I feel—or did until Chorley told me. He is dead serious, and he is not a man to exaggerate."

"That would be the kindling for war. But even assuming that our military hawks wanted to do such a thing, why would they let a curator and a writer know about it beforehand?"

"To go outside official channels and to put the facts and threats out on a more personal basis."

"So that—if I remember your old phrase correctly —*our* asses would be in a sling, not theirs."

Linkum nodded. "That's one way of putting it. Another, fancier one is that we would serve as conduits for a tradeoff of information."

Glazunov said, "So far you've made it a one-sided proposition. What's the trade?"

"Hap Chorley wants the GRU to know that the Americans also have an unconventional weapon that could cause grave damage somewhere in the Soviet Union."

"And how, capitano, would the Pentagon attack us —by what means?"

"Andrei, I don't know the operational details. But Hap Chorley is prepared to exchange written information: Your plan for our plan. Exchanging secrets? No, of course not. But general knowledge leading to neutralization? Yes."

Glazunov laughed. "Oh, yes, the Carthaginians and Romans tell each other about their latest spears and longbows, thereby preventing the Punic Wars."

Linkum made a sweeping gesture around the valley.

"Well, this dead civilization is the right place to look into the future of the next war. I don't blame you for thinking it's all pretty far-fetched. But if I didn't believe there was some chance of success I wouldn't be sitting here."

Glazunov put his arm on Linkum's shoulder.

"At least we're in the realm of the probable, not just the possible," Linkum went on. "About war by other means. About incredible, scientific developments by academicians who have been bought with grants and fellowships to work for the Pentagon. I know and you know that there are men in both our countries who not only think about the unthinkable but, by doing so, help make it inevitable. If you and I can do something to stop their Doomsday . . . well, we would sort of be picking up where we left off in the final days of our war."

Glazunov said, "I believe in science, and I believe in fiction, and I believe in science-fiction, which cancels out both. We have many science-fiction books written in my country because one can say things about other planets that we cannot about our own. What you're describing sounds like one of those futuristic tales that come true."

"It's more urgent, Andrei. Chorley himself believes it's imminent—even weeks from now. That's why we— both of us—have to move quickly."

Glazunov stood up, and then began to walk down the roadway to their car. There was movement below. As they drew closer to the cafe's parking places below the temple, the automobiles tailing them suddenly and independently took off in the direction of Trapani, then halted, their motors running.

"Back to Palermo, chauffeur," Glazunov said, as he and Linkum settled in the back seat. "We must not allow those two drivers to get lost." The chauffeur smiled. A mile or so behind them, the KGB and CIA cars followed at a not too discreet distance. "Take the Monte Pellegrino road and drop off this gentlemen at the Palme before leaving me at the Villa Igiea."

They drove in silence along the mountain highway and into the environs of the city.

"Let me think about your proposition," Glazunov said, as they approached the Palme. "Overnight, I should say."

"Do you think you can get clearance from here? I assume that this would go through your next-in-line."

"If necessary I can communicate via my Aeroflot captain, but how I do so and to whom would require more thought. This is not a good subject for discussion at this moment, you understand?" Linkum understood; the chauffeur might know more English than he dared show. "Or, I may decide to communicate with you in some other way." In front of the Palme, Glazunov said out of earshot of the chauffeur, "Tomorrow at eight in the morning, meet me inside the woodcarver's shop that faces the entrance of the Villa Igiea. Take a taxi there so we won't disturb the gumshoes. I'll give you my answer then—agreed?"

Linkum nodded. They shook hands. Glazunov stepped into the car. It began to roll off but then halted halfway up the Via Roma. The Soviet curator got out and entered the hotel lobby. He sauntered around the statuary.

"I just had to see those marble titties once more," Glazunov said to the startled Linkum, who was waiting for the tired elevator.

Then, grinning and waving, he as suddenly departed.

That morning, Linkum rose with the sun instead of the rumbling trucks. He felt the surging excitement that always took hold of him when he was chasing a story around the Mediterranean. Only now, he realized, he was not an outsider looking in but a participant. It was frightening; but chasing stories often could be foolish and foolhardy, a business for boys instead of grownups. It was your legs and your sentences that had to be durable and inventive; you were forever running, forever behind; lied to; fawning for scraps of information; told only what would make officialdom look good; listening and acting as if you already knew the answers; promising tradeoffs but knowing that if you did it right you would have to betray the smooth and friendly scoundrels; unscholarly and without the time to research or put anything into perspective—or to break off a story that had proved groundless; a victim of the incessant daily momentum; welding bits and pieces into the style you had built up over the years: scrap irony.

Now there was nowhere to put those skills of bluff and bravado into print. It was different on the other side —Hap Chorley's side, maybe Andrei Glazunov's side. He knew there were no choices, at the moment, and that he had to ignite his energies, not, for God's sake, to save the world singlehandedly, but to salvage his own life. Anybody could save the world.

He stared at the high ceiling and followed the double line of plaster rosettes circling overhead. The rosettes and the dark mustiness called up memories . . . After their marriage, he and Elena had stayed at the Grande Albergo e delle Palme openly as they had done furtively during those precious Saturdays of wartime lovemaking. Now the elders of the Florio family were gone; the cousins had long since departed for menial jobs in Germany; and his Antonio, his son, was dead.

After taking breakfast in his room, he walked a few blocks to avoid a watched taxicab too close to the hotel. When he arrived in front of the Villa Igiea, he noticed that some of the crew members of the Aeroflot IL-62M were talking to Glazunov. Everything appeared to be cool. Glazunov greeted him openly, in English. The crew drove off toward Punta Raisi airport, leaving them alone.

"We've got very little time, my friend," Glazunov said. "They're coming back to pick me up with the captain—an old pilot from our war. But first things first."

He rang the twirling iron bell of the woodcarver's shop, entered and bought four angelic figurines that looked like fugitives from a Renaissance high basilica. "Notice how the knot in the wood is retained to serve as a counterpull to the angel," he said, lightly showing off his curatorial knowledge. Then he took out a roll of lire and negotiated for a smaller version of the iron bell.

"I see that you're still buying Mickey Mouse watches," Linkum said.

"Oh, no, this is peasant art even if they don't know it. This gentleman's grandfather probably carved them the same way a hundred years ago."

Linkum nodded. "By the way," he said, "what else is new?"

"What else is new is that you are invited to visit me in Leningrad, Sam. You will be my guest, the guest of the government. You can be writing about the new exhibition that I'm mounting for your art magazine, correct?"

"And what exhibition are you talking about?"

"I haven't dreamed one up yet, but I will. Maybe one on military paintings from your country and mine done by artists in the field?"

"I guess that's as good a cover story as any."

"What do you mean, capitano? It won't be just a sham, I'll make it a reality."

"It's not too bad an idea at that—as long as it comes out that you didn't win the war all alone."

"We have an old Ukranian saying—nuts to you."

"Ukranian-American. Were you able to get clearance this fast? You must be a bigger operator than I thought you were."

"My next-above has been radioed and given clearance for your visit. I was surprised, but my next-above didn't seem to be."

"What's his name and rank?"

"I didn't say it was a him—or a her. You know that it's the sort of information I couldn't tell you even if—"

"Well, the only reason I asked specifically is that you already have been told Hap Chorley's name. I'm sure he'll ask me when I get back."

"We do things a little differently in my country, Sam."

"How will we be in touch on details?"

"I think you will receive an invitation from the Washington embassy of the Soviet Union to attend the exhibition at the Hermitage. Just a routine matter. It might also be sent to others—only they'll receive their invitation a little too late for arrangements to be made."

"I'll have to clear anything with Hap Chorley. I've been out of this business too long to know how it's handled officially. But I suspect that the fewer people who know, the better. It isn't a matter of embassies—yours or ours."

"I agree, but I just cannot write you a letter or make a telephone call. For obvious reasons." Glazunov paused. "I'll figure out a way that's simpler. The best is still a courier—one person, acting alone."

"How would I recognize him—or her?"

Glazunov reached into his pocket and pulled out two colored postcards of Antonello's *"L'Annunziata."* They were labeled part of the Hermitage's collection of Western European art.

"One for you, the other for whoever speaks for me," Glazunov said. "We'll put the Madonna to work for peace, right? The unseen Prince or Princess of Peace. I'm talking art, not religion, you understand."

"I'm willing to talk peace," Linkum said, taking the card.

Glazunov nodded.

In the turn of the roadway one curving hill in the distance, they saw the airport bus returning.

"Maybe what we are trying to do is a little crazy, Sam, yet—"

"Less crazy than my radiating you with a neutron bomb and you in turn doing the same to me."

Glazunov smiled. "Two civilized nations like Russia

and France would never dream of doing that to each other, would they?"

Linkum said, "Which war are we up to, Andrei?"

"Tolstoy's, of course. Do you remember how we used to read passages from the worn little books we carried in our rucksacks? Leningrad, the Battle of the Bulge, Verdun, the Battle of Borodino—mix them all together. Borodino: *Through the smoke could be caught glimpses of something black, probably men, and sometimes the gleam of bayonets. But whether they were stationary or moving, whether they were French or Russian, could not be seen.*"

"I had my favorite lines, too. Don't hold me to the exact translation, but on the eve of the same battle Prince Andrew said something like this: *The aim of war is murder, the methods of war are spying, treachery, the ruin of a country's inhabitants, fraud and falsehood termed military craft*—or was it *glory?*"

"Very close, capitano. And do you know how that ends?"

"I've forgotten."

"Count Tolstoy, that saboteur of royal wars, went on: *All the kings, except the Chinese, wear military uniforms, and he who kills most people receives the highest awards.*"

"I wonder how he knew so much about the Chinese?"

"The Chinese—well, that's another story to save for the next time. Here's my ride to the airport. The pilot of my plane should be down any moment, but I don't think it would be useful to introduce you. So I'll say my goodbye now. Don't forget your souvenir postcard. We'll see one another very soon, okay?"

114

They shook hands; and then embraced.

As the captain of the Aeroflot IL-62M came through the portals of the Villa Igiea, Linkum disappeared behind the woodcarver's stringed angels and cherubim.

Five

"**T**HE FISH IS on the hook," Hap Chorley said. "Now, we've got to play him for all it's worth."

Sam Linkum shook his head.

"You're using the wrong terminology. Glazunov isn't a minnow and I'm not going to treat him like a catch. That wasn't the deal—and it isn't the way I work."

"You want to quibble about kid-glove language or treatment? Okay, but this is the Pentagon, not the State Department. And I'll be the judge of what can work operationally, not you."

"You mean that *you're* the fisherman and *I'm* on the hook."

"Sam, let's not play games with each other. We're on the same side, remember? I said that, insofar as it's humanly possible, I want to take you out of harm's way. To do so I have to be—and so do you, friend—very cold-assed. Now, let's get back on track. Try to recall the exact words and phrases that he used about me. By the way, were you wired?"

"No, and neither was Glazunov."

"How do you know, did you ask him politely?"

"Not even impolitely, but we embraced when we said our goodbyes. Both of us would have felt the apparatus and, frankly, both of us were feeling for it. He didn't have any, unless it was hidden up his crotch, and I deliberately didn't, knowing that an old pro would check me out."

"Now you're talking sense. I'm glad you're at least skeptical and I'm glad you have confidence in the Russsky —up to a point. What about when you two were alone in Segesta?"

"Too much wind up there, even in warm weather it blows out of Africa. It would rip apart any sound. We both knew that and, anyway, he didn't know my proposition beforehand."

"It's important to know how much he knew about me and the Air Force Security Service. Did he mention the Defense Intelligence Agency or anything about ELINT? How do you gauge his knowledge of me?"

"He himself didn't seem to know details about Defense. The immediate reaction to anything sounding like intelligence is CIA. When your name came up, he remembered you as the fat major—that's his exact description, as long as you asked—who smoked foul-smelling cigars."

"Up his ass," Chorley said, lighting a Romeo y Julieta. "These are fresher than the ones from Havana at the Moskva or Metropole. And all that fat was muscle then. But I'm just as happy that every move they hear about is considered a CIA thing. You straightened him out, didn't you, about who we are? Because it's part of our plan to deal on the military level with our opposite numbers and not with the yo-yos."

"Right, I said Air Force intelligence but without details. How the hell could I when I don't know the details myself?"

"You know enough."

"By the way, there was one thing. When I said Pentagon, he assumed it was the Army Security Agency."

"Jesus H. Christ! That's just what I was asking you to recall. What else?"

"Glazunov said that his next-above had approved a trip by me to Leningrad."

"And who is his next-above—did he say?"

"He said he wouldn't say."

"I'll tell you if he won't because you'll be dealing with her. Yes, it's a her, and she's got three balls, like your lady vice president at the network who's in charge of ball-cutting. Nadejda Zaremba. From what you've told me, your asshole buddy isn't quite as innocent and detached as you make him out to be. Western art curator, and all that crap. His reserve status sounds pretty active to me. He can get on the horn in Palermo and get an answer back from Moscow in less than twenty-four hours. Maybe we didn't check him out enough. Did you happen to notice if he had any women with him, like a wife?"

"No, he was alone."

"Because we've had reports that he's a skirt-chaser when he leaves the motherland."

"That doesn't sound unusual—what's it got to do with our operation?"

"It can sometimes be useful. You know how, that hasn't changed in our line of work."

Chorley unwound his frame from the desk, walked to the window and looked through his binoculars toward the marble monuments of Washington across the river. Then he turned and said, "Sam, you'll have to keep your pecker up and your antennae out at all times. I'm less concerned about Glazunov than I am about Madame Zaremba. Or, rather, General Zaremba. She's the highest-ranking muckamuck in the GRU's intelligence directorate. A brilliant mathematician with a computer where her heart and tits should be. Never been outside the Soviet Union, a pure product of the system. She's probably checking you out right now."

"How? Here or there?"

"Oh, by doing what I'm doing with you—debriefing Glazunov."

"There isn't much to know. A thousand forgotten bylines stuck away in several dead newspaper morgues that have been microfilmed or microfiched so that no one can use them. The rest of me is routine, dull. *Vin ordinaire.*"

"Did you tell Glazunov much about your personal life?"

"Nothing beyond the straight stuff. I'm sure they never took pictures of me entering my favorite restaurant with a friend. He does know that my son was killed in Vietnam."

"How come?"

"I told him—it's no secret."

"I wish you hadn't. It's none of their fucking business. They're liable to think you're bitter about your country. *Our* country."

"In a way, I am."

Chorley's face began to redden. He started to speak, then cut himself off. He snapped his fingers angrily.

After a few moments, he broke the silence. "You know, Sam, a country's intelligence apparatus works the same way as a handful of chips in a high-stakes poker game. Each one counts. In this particular operation, we only hold a few high cards in our hands. Some of them we put on the table, others we have to keep to ourselves. The other side is always looking for places where we show signs of weakness. Tell them a personal fact the way you did and it can come back to haunt you. All of us have to bury our feelings for the good of this operation. The end-result is what's going to count. This is just about—hell, it *is*—the biggest test of will in the history of our two countries. I'm not flag-waving on you. I'm just trying to separate out the emotions from the actions."

"Hap, I wouldn't have gotten this far in gaining Glazunov's confidence unless I'd renewed our friendship in personal terms."

"Could be—but you're dealing with an old pro. Don't be conned by his charm. He and his people don't give a shit about you personally. But if they think you're

embittered, they can begin to think of you as vulnerable
—reachable."

"Do you?" Linkum did not hide his irritation.

"I'm not them. You wouldn't be sitting here unless
I had confidence in you. Ours is a business of blinking
first. We don't want to do anything or show anything
that will put wrong ideas into their heads. The next
thing you know, they're encouraged to behave as if
they've just taken a big snootful of ninety-octane vodka
and can lick anyone in the house. And that's why, old
cock, I say that you committed a tactical error that
should not be repeated."

Linkum stared at Chorley, making sure not to blink.

"Now the next step," Chorley said, pursuing his
advantage, "is to sit tight and wait for your signal."

"From them—or from you?"

"From them. I don't give signals—I give orders."

Linkum nodded. In for a penny, in for a pound.
What the hell, maybe it was better to be on the receiving
end of the orders, you didn't always have to pretend you
knew what you were up to.

"And when do you expect me to get the signal from
them?"

"Tomorrow. So my source tells me, and he's got a
pretty good track record. Don't ask me who or how.
Now, the gent who's going to approach you will be
coming from the Bulgarian Embassy on Sixteenth and V
Street. Make it easy for him: Go from your hotel in
Georgetown by taxicab to Meridian Hill Park, and sit on
a park bench where Sixteenth meets Florida Avenue.
You'll be tailed by them. The Bulgarian is a youngish

fellow and he usually carries a copy of *Playboy* or *Penthouse* or one of the other skin magazines. He'll sit down on the bench and flash the Antonello postcard. You pull yours out of your pocket. Then he'll give you an envelope—and you give him this one that I've prepared for you."

Chorley handed Linkum a sealed envelope without markings.

"Am I supposed to know what's inside it?"

"No problem—simply where I think your next rendezvous should be. For your benefit. Don't let him get away without giving it to him. He won't expect a reply so fast."

The next morning Linkum left the Georgetown Dutch Inn after a country-style breakfast that included baked pineapple on link sausage on scrambled eggs, and relish on the side; he often ate crazily off the menu in Washington, which always struck him as a sleepy Southern town disguised behind a national front of marble and limestone. With maple syrup on top.

Chorley's instructions were easy to follow. But the benches on the right corner of Meridian Hill Park were taken by a delegation of ID-tagged Georgia teachers in rhinestone-rimmed glasses under tight perms and wearing sensible white pumps, resting between visits to the FBI's shooting gallery in the J. Edgar Hoover Memorial Building and to other public relations wonders of Washington.

Linkum leaned against a ginkgo tree, and waited. From the corner of his eye he noticed a burly figure

123

approaching. He kept his head down. The man was carrying a copy of *The Washington Post*. But his shoes were a clue: heavy-looking clodhoppers with cleated rubber soles and oversized eyelets; black shoes with brown corduroy trousers seemed right for a Bulgarian.

Linkum removed the colored postcard from his jacket and casually examined it so that the Madonna was visible. The Bulgarian strolled by, looked around him, then stopped, turned back, and brought forth his matching Antonello.

"Ho-kay?" the Bulgarian said, grinning.

There couldn't have been a second one in Washington.

"Okay," Linkum replied.

He tried to remember if he had ever met a Bulgarian before. This one looked like a lieutenant or captain out of uniform whose wife cut his hair every Sunday night after the bath. He didn't shop at Garfinckel's, but he wore a pleasant air.

The Bulgarian shielded himself from the street and its parked cars and handed Linkum a small brown envelope. Without waiting, he walked quickly toward Florida Avenue. Linkum went after him and gripped his arm.

"This one is for you, chum," he said, attempting to thrust the envelope into the Bulgarian's hand.

The Bulgarian seemed confused. He shook his head.

"One for you, one for me, understand? Deliver this to your boss."

Obviously, the Bulgarian had not been instructed to

receive anything, but Chorley had said not to let him get away without it.

"It's okay," Linkum said.

That seemed to be a reassuring code word. "Hokay?" The Bulgarian peered around the park and, once again, blocked himself from the vision of anyone in the street.

He accepted the envelope and placed it inside his jacket, accidentally dropping the newspaper he was carrying. From inside its sports section, two folded copies of magazines fell out: *Hustler* and *Penthouse*. The Bulgarian scooped them up and hurried off.

"It went off just as you said—including the skin magazines."

"Let's see how close I came to guessing their response."

Linkum handed the brown envelope to Chorley, who placed it under a high-powered microscope that was concealed behind a row of Strategic Air Command bombing reports. "No microdot lettering that I can spot," Chorley said. Linkum had known enough not to open the envelope himself; his mind called up some of the little security steps they used to take when handling enemy material: the search for the unseen message within the message.

Chorley now slit open the envelope with a pocket penknife, read the contents of the single sheet. "No dice." He handed it to Linkum. The typed message read:

THE HERMITAGE MOST CORDIALLY INVITES MR. SAM LIN-

125

KUM DISTINGUISHED ART CRITIC TO ATTEND OPENING OF NEW EXHIBITION OF WESTERN EUROPEAN AND AMERICAN PAINTINGS. RESERVATION FIRST WEEK IN APRIL AT EVROPEISKAYA HOTEL AS GUEST OF CURATOR. SIGNED GLAZUNOV.

"What do you mean, no dice? Isn't this the signal we were waiting for?"

"Sam, I said we were baiting them first. The fish has to be on the hook, but we have to be on the playing end of the line. I don't want to see *you* hooked in the Neva River."

"All right, general, what's my next move?"

"Can the sarcasm, friend."

"Well, not keeping me fully informed turns me into a dumb courier, like your Bulgarian prat-boy. I've put my trust in you. At least for this operation. I had to chase the Bulgarian down the street—he didn't expect anything."

"Don't worry about him, he does what he's told. One day, when we have to, we'll turn him. He's crazy about tall, blond American ass. But not yet. Right now, my message is on the way to Moscow. It'll straighten things."

"Well, I'm glad they know something I don't know."

"My message will straighten things out. I anticipated Glazunov's—or, rather, Madame Zaremba's—invitation to you. I simply said thanks, but it would be more convenient for you two art experts to have a preliminary meeting somewhere else. In the West. Venice. Because you had to report on some event taking place there that would be of great interest to Glazunov as well. I trust that you don't mind that I signed your name to the message."

"I don't mind—as long as you tell me first."

"So far, so good. You'll get to Moscow, but I want there to be a way-stop first in the West. I don't want you tracked while I'm kept in the dark. They've got all the surveillance there, and we can't keep an eye on you, or them, without blowing the cover of some of our friends. In Venice, we've got our own people. I want you to test the waters—to see if the GRU is willing to make a deal with me. They'll get their information from us as soon as I know that their military intelligence is willing to play along—to be as anti-confrontation as you and I are."

Linkum nodded. "You make it sound as if the military intelligence top brass are the good guys. That's a switch."

"That's the *reality*. It's a risk, but I know my job. I know the approximate mentality of the people in the GRU who are doing the same thing, and I know the horses' asses I'm supposed to share my information with in the CIA. No way."

Chorley hit his intercom. "Maryjane, be a good girl, honey, and bring in two cups of java." She placed them in front of the two men, asked if they wanted any "munchies," and walked out rhythmically. "It must be jelly 'cause jam don't shake like that," Chorley observed, and Linkum said, "You're dating yourself, Hap," and Chorley grinned and said, "They can't make keesters like that in the Communist countries."

127

"How soon do you expect them to answer your proposal?"

"Momentarily. The signal is on its way—we've tracked it via ELINT. They've already got it at Number Two Dzerzhinsky Square. Probably won't have to pass it on to your buddy at the Hermitage—he'll obey orders. We're not very good on the lines between Moscow and Leningrad. They've bugged and monitored our behinds every which way so it's not much use to let them know how much we can pick up. Actually, the slowest part was the trip down Sixteenth Street from the Bulgarian to the Russian Embassy. It took the shithead in the crewcut nearly an hour because he stopped off at the drugstore to check out the latest tits-and-ass magazines."

Linkum hesitated for a moment, then said, "Do you think I'd have time to go up to New York and see Jennie Ives?"

"I'd prefer it if you didn't this time."

"What about a phone call—just to check in?"

"Worse—the lines have ears."

"Then what do you mean that you *prefer* I don't?"

"Sam, when I say something like that I'm being polite with an old friend. What I'm saying is, *No.*" He paused. "I can get word to her that you're okay and will be in touch—"

"Absolutely not. She's my business, not Air Force blue-sky hugger-mugger."

"Up to you, Sam. I was trying to be helpful under the circumstances."

"Where do you want me to stay until we get the word?"

"At my farm in Maryland. Just a matter of security. The larder is full. It'll probably be just a one-night, at the most two-night, stand."

"Hap, I want to emphasize what I just said—leave Jennie out of the deal. No surveillance, no nothing. You have my word that I won't call her. Because if I find out that she's been touched by any of what I'm doing for you, the game's over."

Two nights later, riding piggyback, Sam Linkum was flown in an unmarked jet trainer to Westover Field near Chicopee Falls, Massachusetts. There he boarded a Military Air Transport Command early model, passenger-converted B-52 that had run out of steam after three hundred bombing strikes over the ricefields of Southeast Asia. He landed after dark on the NATO side of Malpensa Airport outside Milan. Being Italians first, the Communist-dominated regime had winked and permitted the Americans to use the far side of the field, for an exorbitant fee and no questions asked. The trans-Atlantic flight had been eerie: he was the only passenger on board.

Malpensa. Was that someone's honored name or did it combine two words: *Bad thoughts?* He resolved to find out sometime. Why hadn't they named LaGuardia Airport *Fiorello?* Then you could take the *Little Flower* shuttle to Washington or Boston. His high had returned, along with the silliness and wandering imagination, the high he always experienced the moment the plane circumnavigated the moon and parted the clouds and touched down, and the warm air over the Mediterranean's burnished seas penetrated his pores. His engine, sparked by memory, started to run again.

A gray Fiat 1500 pulled up alongside the parked B-52 and an American Air Force officer of indeterminate rank greeted him with a halting salute and a curt, "Good evening, sir." Linkum stepped inside the proferred door; the officer himself drove off immediately, picking up the autostrada and speeding through Brescia, Verona, Vicenza and Padua. Linkum's attempt at civility, even about the officer's home town, was turned aside. Hap Chorley's professionals knew how to keep their mouths shut; maybe Hap was sending him a long-distance subliminal message.

There was a motor launch waiting—"All taken care of, sir"—that took him from the quay near the garage terminal through the narrow, backwater *rii* leading out to the Canale della Giudecca. The cowboy at the wheel of the motoscafo, which Linkum noticed was named *Alberto III*, made waves against the night-anchored steamers, showing his style and superiority by speed. Alberto volunteered that he owned a fleet of three motor launches. At least he wasn't afraid to talk. "Americano or English?" he enquired, and when Linkum responded, he said, "But of course, I have the great admiration for Americani—they are more sympathetic." He did not explain why. As the launch slowed and circled the San Marco side of Giudecca, Linkum looked over his shoulder and glimpsed the golden dome of S. Maria della Salute, a pale half-moon of stunning light and shadow. Alberto docked his *Alberto III* at the Cipriani, the luxury hotel at the tip of Giudecca Island. Hap had asked him where he wanted to stay, and when he said anywhere but around the noise of San Marco Square, he was told it would be the Cipriani. "We get cooperation there," Chorley said casually, and by now Linkum knew enough not to press him for details. At the landing, he over-tipped Alberto. The motoscafo mogul handed him his business card, said he was always available "for friends" to undertake special assignments, and roared off into the dying night.

Linkum woke up to a ringing telephone.
"Capitano Sam? Capitano Glazunov here."
"Andrei? Where the hell are you staying?"
"The same as you—the Cipriani."
"Shall I come to your room or you to mine?"

If Hap Chorley had said that the management here was "cooperative," he probably meant that they would be watched if not tuned in anywhere in the hotel. He wished that he wasn't so sleepy—and that Chorley had been willing to share a little more information. But it was the nature of the silent service—not submarines, intelligence—to keep routines and directions even from your associates. Certainly he should not have been sur-prised by Andrei's location; that should have been in his last-minute briefing at Chorley's Maryland farmhouse.

Linkum rubbed sleep out of his jetlagged eyes. He was hungry. They decided to meet on the terrace of the Cipriani, overlooking the tiny island of San Giorgio, for late breakfast. The less than romantic smell of the lagoon filled the air but he never minded it here: it was as much

131

a part of Venice as the Byzantine cupolas and winged lions and tired fiddlers in front of Florian's.

They embraced like old friends.

"I am famished," Glazunov said. "As I get older, food counts more with me—a sensual pleasure. Where the hell have you been? I've been walking around waiting for you for a day and a half."

"It takes a little longer to fly here from the States. Besides, I didn't expect to see you at this fancy place. But I should have known better—you always travel first cabin. You're a true capitalist in your bones, Andrei."

"We have a saying in Leningrad that we don't say out loud too often: Inside every party member a capitalist heart beats. I changed locations when I heard you were staying here."

Glazunov did not say who had told him; and Linkum did not ask.

"They were going to put me up at the Soviet trade mission here but—"

"But you didn't want to be spied on, right?"

Glazunov laughed.

"Not exactly, but close enough. I wanted to be on my own in a pleasure palazzo, just like you rich Americanski. Now, let's eat."

In his near-perfect Italian, Glazunov summoned the waiter, who told him it was too late for breakfast and, when he then asked for lunch, he was informed it was too early. He demanded to see the manager who arrived in a flurry of shooting sleeves, assessed the personality counterweights and bawled out the malingering waiter. "How many eggs, sir, one or two?" asked the manager, and Glazunov told him, "Eggs, not one or two, bring eggs!" The manager issued orders, shifted the burden of his reproach to the assembled waiters, adjusted his tie and flounced out of the garden terrace.

Glazunov shook his head. "Everything in this country is still *bella figura*. The Communist Party can change the government but they can't change the posturing."

Suddenly there was a commotion alongside the Cipriani's private dock.

A man's body, fully clothed, was being fished out of the Canale della Grazia.

In a matter of moments, two Venetian police launches pulled up at the dock.

"Can anyone here identify this man?" the police enquired.

"He's not a guest, surely," the manager said quickly.

"And not one of our staff, for certain," his assistant said. "He should be removed from the property instantly."

The hotelkeepers did not want corpses on the premises.

An old pensioner who caught the launch lines and assisted the debarking passengers for a few coins looked at the body. "Why, it's Alberto!" He looked around him for approval and met stares of silence. "Alberto Giobbe, the owner of the motoscafo, you all know him, don't you?" The manager shrugged. "None of us ever saw him before—he is not from the Cipriani's private launch service." The pensioner went on anyway. "The one we used to caution about speeding and cutting off his motor, remember?" The manager signaled to one of the waiters to bring a tablecloth to cover the body. The police took down the name and called for the hospital launch.

Linkum and Glazunov went back to their table, where a bowl of hardboiled eggs awaited them.

"I'm not hungry any more," Linkum said.

"Peasant fare—I did not want overcooked hardboiled eggs," Glazunov said. "Let's get off the island and head for the Accademia Gallery. We can find something to eat nearby without any corpses floating by."

Linkum excused himself for a moment to go to his room, saying that he had to change into walking shoes and pick up a sweater. Glazunov's room, by chance, was one floor directly below his. He locked the door behind him, and looked for the business card that he vaguely remembered placing in the pocket of his over-the-arm raincoat in the pre-dawn hours. It was still there:

ALBERTO GIOBBE, SPECIAL SERVICES,
PRIVATE LAUNCHES, TEL. 46.62.396

He suspected that Signor Giobbe had picked up the wrong person for his health: himself. The trip arranged by the Air Force officer had been "all taken care of," less fat tip, but there would be no more special services through the backwater *rii* of Venice for Americani. Whoever had decided to send him a warning in the form of a very wet corpse had succeeded. He wondered why such a minor, talkative person was singled out as an example; and by whom—and should he inform Hap Chorley right away? Of course, it could have been an accident. Happened here all the time. Of course, and Alberto was a crazy speed demon. But, he told himself, this was no accident.

Making a note of the telephone number in his address book, under another name, Linkum put a match to the business card and flushed the ashes down the toilet.

The curator from the Hermitage and the journalist for the obscure art journal caught the *vaporetto* to the Accademia stop. Crowds of students and tourist-explainers blocked the lower level of paintings from sight, but a second and sometimes a third level reached to the crenelated ceilings. Glazunov unscrewed his telescope to study the masterpeices. A guard came up and said cameras and binoculars were forbidden in the galleries. Glazunov pulled out his identification and a letter from the Accademia's director. The guard, who carried a copy of *L'Unità*, the Communist daily, apologized.

"I would trade three of my early Picassos for that one Giorgione," Glazunov said. "Here, look at the detail in the sky with my glass."

"This is as good a place as any to be alone," Linkum said. "We're even here—no corpses except in the paintings, no walls with ears."

"The reproductions are always false. If they put in too much brown in the foreground, you get the flesh tones of the mother nursing the child but you lose the lightning bolt in the sky behind them."

"Hap Chorley wanted me to tell you that we're ready to move on the information that will help us both. Help our superiors, that is."

"Unless the balance between the colors of nature and the colors of the humans is perfect, you lose the significance of *La Tempesta* altogether. Giorgione achieved the poetic harmony between both."

"Hap, by the way, sent his best regards to you. What he wanted to know in particular was if his message had gone through directly to your Madame Zaremba."

"The sixteenth century in particular attained a new summit for the Venetian school. Everything that followed built on what they had achieved."

"And, if so, if she would take his proposition seriously. Now that the lines are open between us, there doesn't seem to be any difficulty about passing information on our level between the two intelligence services."

"Giorgione and the others had to invent the new world that always existed and put it on the walls of churches and in these huge canvases, disguised as religion. It could only have happened in a commercial state like Venice where the doges outnumbered the bishops."

"Have you spoken directly to Madame Zaremba? Or to someone in the GRU's Fifth Directorate? Because I know Hap is going to ask me if we're on the right wavelength."

"What should interest you as a writer is that while the Venetians were doing all this on canvas, Shakespeare was achieving the same on stage. Perhaps that is why his best dramas are set in Italy."

"What's up, friend?"

"Well, this is my second visit here in twenty-four hours," Glazunov said, still deliberately evading. "I don't like to look at more than one or two paintings at a time. Why don't we move on to Peggy Guggenheim's palace? I have something to show you there."

"I mean, what's the gag? You're not exactly being responsive."

Glazunov looked at his watch. "We can see her collection if we walk there quickly. This is one of the afternoons when it's open."

Linkum shrugged. They were both in Venice for the same reason: it was not to see art or even each other. The candybox on wooden stilts that was Venice always seemed to unhinge minds.

Linkum had never been inside the Palazzo Venier—the Guggenheim collection there had always been closed at the time he was free—but he had read about the walls of Paul Klees and Jackson Pollacks that she had accumulated. With Glazunov as his guide, they hurried through the half-built palace.

"In my country it would be called degenerate art," Glazunov remarked, "but I must be degenerate myself because I like it. Klee, Pollack, Moore, Calder—they were twentieth-century revolutionaries. But I must show you the most amusing scupture in the collection."

Facing the canal was one of Marino Marini's horse and riders. The barebacked male had an expression of glee and a modest erection. "Marini made the cock detachable so it could be screwed out when nuns came by with schoolchildren," Glazunov said, "but the word got around and it was stolen. So were its replacements. Now it's permanent. Very degenerate, you Western cold warriors. We'll bury you, as one of our leaders once said." He paused. "By the way, that permanent erection reminds me that I have an appointment for dinner tonight with one of the secretaries at the Soviet trade mission."

"Will I see you later this evening?"

"Not if my appointment works out the way it

should. We can talk about the other matter tomorrow morning."

"You don't seem to be in a hurry. Are we both whistling in the dark?"

"I don't know that American phrase—what do you mean?"

"That if what Hap Chorley says is so, we have no time to waste."

"You're speaking like a journalist, not a bureaucrat, Sam. Let's postpone the Third World War for another day. Go out and have some fun."

"I'll see you in the morning, Andrei."

Linkum walked alone through the twisting streets, his nostrils twitching alongside the brackish canals, until it grew dark. The heels of unseen strollers struck suspiciously against echoing alleyways. His presence was known. One tail was not so serious, but two could be distinctly dangerous if he was cornered. It was no longer simply them against us; in these western republics of Europe that were theoretical client-states of the United States or the Soviet Union, political parties spun off in wild, undisciplined directions and terrorists failed to live by the rules of civilized killing.

He quickened his pace, and emerged through the delicate columns of the arcades and followed the street lamps to the Grand Canal. With the sequined guests, he waited at the small private pier and caught the turn-around launch back to the Cipriani, where inconvenient corpses were quickly disposed of.

A slip of paper in his key slot at the concierge's desk bore a message: Call the Guardi Art Company in Maryland. Any telephone number? he asked, trying to determine how much was known by the man running the desk and if the number could be found with folding money, but the little tyrant with his crossed keys symbol of authority shrugged and shook his head. At this hour the call must have come from the farm. He looked at the words on the message slip. Hap Chorley had not yet lost his sense of fun.

Linkum returned to the dock and took the launch back to San Marco and walked over to the Danieli Royal Excelsior. He slipped the night concierge a twenty-dollar bill and placed a call from one of the private booths off the ornate lobby. Hap Chorley got on the line in less than a minute.

"Did you buy any valuable prints for our firm?"

"Not yet, but I have a good prospect, I think."

"Where are you calling me from at this ungodly hour?"

"The Danieli. I didn't think it was wise to get back to you from the Cipriani—they found a floater there. The guy who was set up by our contact in Milano. The motoscafo owner, face down, no marks on the body. A friend of ours—"

"Not exactly—more of an acquaintance. Don't bother mentioning his name. I know who you're referring to. I'm not too surprised. But let's get on with the firm's business."

"Wait a minute. Is there something more I should know about the incident, something involving me?"

"Don't worry your head about it, chum. It was an accident, happens all the time."

139

"You knew about it before I called?"

"Well, yes—that's how it was reported to the hospital authorities and police in Venice. I heard. Too bad. Next time, take a gondola."

"You didn't happen to know about it *before* the police by any chance, did you?What the hell's going on?"

"I told you to put it out of your mind. The floater was a talkative fellow—and he talked out of both sides of his mouth."

Linkum said, "Meaning what?"

"The trouble was, he was a secret idealist, and idealists are not to be trusted in our line of work. I prefer someone who can be turned by a slut, not a slogan."

"And that's why he was—"

"You didn't hear me say that, chum. But we suspected that they'd reached him and so he'd lost his usefulness. More than that, in fact. I didn't want to put you in more danger by getting you too near one of the crazies from the party."

Linkum kept silent. After a moment Chorley said, "We can discuss any gripes you have in person. The one thing—no, two things—that concern me now is the reaction of the person our firm is doing business with to the poor fellow's demise and where we stand in moving ahead on our program." Linkum told Chorley that the man from the Hermitage seemed as surprised as himself when the motoscafo owner was fished out of the Canale della Grazia.

"And where do you stand otherwise with our friend?"

"I'll know more in the morning. He may be waiting

for instructions. He was a little evasive but easygoing—
we did the museums together. You're spending your
money well on my education in High Renaissance art."

"Well, chum, I don't mind side benefits, so long as
you keep your eye on the main chance. Keep your pecker
up and call me here, not at my usual workplace, tomorrow night about the same time. By the way, where is our
friend at this moment?"

"Relaxing with one of the secretaries from his trade
mission."

Chorley laughed. "It figures. That evens things up.
They know about your son's death in the Nam and we
now confirm that he's vulnerable in the sack department."

"You've got a charming way of putting things."

"Nothing personal, all I meant to say is that our bio
on him when he leaves the holy motherland checks out.
In my spot, I have to know these details. I'm sorry if I
offended you, Sam—it was thoughtless of me. Relax, get
yourself a night's sleep, what's left of it, and I'll catch
you later."

Walking through the lobby, Linkum glanced up at
the multicolored marble staircase that had once echoed
to the footsteps of the doges of Venice and their women.
He imagined himself returning here with Jennie Ives,
lying together in a lofty high-ceilinged room facing the
glistening domes and belltowers on the islands, with the
light of the Adriatic breaking through the shuttered windows, ignoring the wakeup call of the sun.

And he had a sudden desire to hear her voice, which
he loved for its softness. He looked at his wristwatch and

subtracted five hours. She might just be winding up her weekly piece for the late edition. The concierge nodded and smiled conspiratorily, and he nodded and gave him another twenty American. He returned to the private booth and called her direct line, using his old international credit card rather than the one Hap Chorley had given him, with its nonexistent company address somewhere in Rock Creek Park, charged to a cover name for the USAFSS.

She answered in her familiar way: "Jennie Ives, here."

He had heard her say it a thousand times; they checked in with each other in the morning, before lunch, afterward, and gave each other their goodnights when apart.

Linkum kept still, holding his breath.

"Anybody there? It's still Jennie Ives here. . . . "

He heard her speak to her seatmates, Dave Golden and Willy Holmes, in the weekly news analysis section, asking them if they were expecting an overseas call from one of the correspondents.

After a moment she got on the line again and said, "Last chance, whoever you are, and we don't accept collect calls, operator."

The phone clicked off. He had not been able to tell her where he was going; and he wondered, hoped, that she might have surmised that he was on the other end, sending her a signal of concern and love. It was a spur-of-the-moment thing; not what Hap Chorley expected from a man supposed to keep his pecker up and antennae out.

He returned to the Cipriani and fell asleep with her

142

voice in his head: "Jennie Ives here. . . . "

A tapping at his door awoke him. He glanced at his watch: noon almost.

Andrei Glazunov entered, fully dressed.

"You must have had a hard night, capitano," he said. "I couldn't awaken you by telephone. Is she hiding in the closet?"

"Look for yourself," Linkum said, yawning. He showered and shaved while Glazunov threw open the blinds and read *L'Unità*. "And how did you make out with your secretary from the trade mission?" Sam asked.

Glazunov grinned. "That's a military secret. I always feel better the morning after. Let us just say she was very patriotic."

"Well, I had no reason to sleep late except museum feet. I enjoyed your lecture at the Accademia. I guess you've had breakfast already. Any corpses show up on the dock this morning?"

"No—but my room was broken into. Was yours?"

"What do you mean?"

"Someone went through my documents, my briefcase was opened when I returned early this morning. There was nothing there to take except some old catalogues and postcards. They were still there, but whoever touched my things didn't seem to care if I knew or not. A sloppy job, or a deliberate warning. Whoever did it only took a few thousand lire I kept as tip money—to make it look like plain robbery."

"Andrei, I guarantee you, I don't know anything about it. I hope that none of the other intelligence services, yours or mine, knows what we're up to. If they did it to you, they hurt me too."

Linkum looked in his closet and went through the pockets of his two suits and raincoat. He examined his hand luggage and papers. Nothing appeared to be missing.

"It could not have been any of the Italians," Glazunov said. "No reason for them to be interested in my things. It surely must have been one of your people because—"

"No, not mine, Andrei. I didn't come this far to play games." But he privately wondered if some CIA idiot hadn't somehow gotten his spook's hand into the soup.

"I had to report what happened to my superiors in Moscow, of course. They were not surprised, and not pleased."

Linkum said, "I just hope this doesn't get in the way of what we're both trying to pull off . . . "

Glazunov looked around the room—first under the telephone, then behind the lagoonscape prints on the walls.

"Why don't we continue talking outside?" he said, finding nothing.

They parked themselves in comfortable beach chairs at the far end of the veranda, away from the voices and bodies showing off near the pool.

"My bosses are interested, Sam. But my orders are to move. They say you have an advantage here and that we cannot do business fairly."

"Why not in Moscow or Leningrad? I'm prepared to go there and do what's necessary to finish up our deal."

Glazunov shrugged.

"We might have done so if this break-in had not occurred. They want a little more time to work it out. I can meet you on our side—in East Berlin."

Just as Hap had wanted to keep an edge by going to Venice, Sam thought . . . "From everything I've heard about the German Democratic Republic, it's still living at the tail end of World War Two and they don't much abide Americans."

"The World War Two part may not be a bad thing, you know. The East Germans haven't made war on anyone, you also know—not in Southeast Asia, not for oil in the Middle East. As for not abiding Americans, you will be my guest in East Berlin. We're respected. I assure you that your briefcase won't be broken into there."

Linkum hesitated.

"What's the point of taking an interim step when we both should be dealing at the top in Washington and Moscow, where the decisions are made? There's a time factor, you know that."

"Because, old friend, my orders are that it's to be East Berlin. Our esteemed ally." Linkum detected a note of sarcasm. "Whether or not you believe me, I am a curator first and last, not a counter-intelligence agent. Let us not forget that you made the proposition to me in Palermo. I in turn passed it on to the proper person in Dzerzhinsky Square. I am just a cog—the same as you, Sam—in the state machinery. So let us get the machinery rolling."

Linkum nodded. There were no options.

"How soon do you want to meet there—on your side of the Wall?"

"Tomorrow. At the latest, the day after. They are prepared for us, and I cannot keep them waiting."

"I'll be there."

Glazunov handed him a telephone number where he could leave a message and be picked up, shook hands and checked out of the Cipriani.

Linkum crossed the water again, found a small hotel with a public telephone and subtracted the trans-Atlantic time. On the other end, he could not raise Hap Chorley but got his automatic recorder. After the given signal, he left the message: *This is your representative from the Guardi firm. Only way I can keep deal alive is to see him on other side—in East Berlin. Phone number given me to contact him there is 930.240.7736. Will be in touch with you when I can. Don't worry yet.*

Hacking around the world, he had reported from most of the magic carpet datelines, the war places and conference tables, but he had never made it to Berlin. It was better to keep your real enemy theoretical; otherwise, feelings of visible humanity might intrude. A few hatreds deserved to be cherished, and Berlin had been the capital of learned death. He had passed up the junkets there by the foundations and tax-exempt think tanks that bought journalists by flattering them into believing their opinions on foreign affairs deserved room and board plus an honorarium. A payoff called an honorarium somehow was linguistic laundering, and he had long ago decided not to be cleansed if the whitewash

146

stuck in his craw afterward. Especially not in the thousand-year Reich.

Linkum caught the British European Airways flight out of Milan the next morning that picked up passengers in Frankfurt and continued across the old Berlin Airlift route to Tempelhof Airport. He piled his luggage and portable typewriter into a shopping cart, which had a sign on it advertising "Dr. Engels Sex-Shops," and wheeled his way to the waiting line of cabs. Except for the gleaming all-black Mercedes-Benz fleet cued up by the numbers, it could have been anywhere on the Continent.

But when he directed the driver to the Berlin Hilton on Budapesterstrasse, a prominent bulge on the uniform of a police officer at a security station crossroads caught his eye and called up the past: a Walther P-38 protruded from the cop's holster. Linkum had owned one once—traded for a carton of Chesterfields with a staff sergeant who had liberated it from a captured colonel in the decimated Hermann Goering Division. On night missions with the underground in the numberless hills around the Mediterranean, he had found it useful simply as a showpiece. The weapon packed a bigger wallop than the shorter-barreled Luger and it delivered notice that the bearer meant business. He had never touched a weapon since then.

After checking in, Linkum again tried to raise Chorley at the Maryland farm; only the recorder answered him. But at least he felt a little more at home here. With the familiar plastic spoons in the paper coffee cups and kalbfleisch burgers (American-style) on the menu, the

147

atmosphere at the Hilton was blandly reassuring. Thinking it might be wise to make his presence known before venturing into East Berlin, he looked up the phone number of the U.S. consulate; and then decided not to call. Hap Chorley didn't trust any of the rival intelligence services let alone those from the other Allied Powers tailing each other in West Germany. He was learning, or rather relearning.

He asked the hotel operator for the number that Glazunov had given him in East Berlin. A woman's voice replied in English, knowing his name and saying that he was expected. He said he was staying at the Hilton. She said that was where all the Americans stayed, but that an all-expenses-paid suite awaited him at the Unter den Linden, courtesy of the German Democratic Republic, because of the article he was writing about the Staatsmuseum. He wondered what story Glazunov had made up about him.

She said, "Your orders are to cross the border immediately."

"Orders? I don't take orders."

"But I am only following my instructions."

"Where is Andrei Glazunov now? I want to speak with him."

"Herr Glazunov is not available."

"Then neither am I until he appears."

She said, after checking someone on her end, "He will contact you as soon as you arrive at the Unter den Linden."

"It's too late this evening, I'm tired, and leave word

with Herr Glazunov that I will cross over in the morning."

A little more calmly now, she said, "Please, Herr Linkum, it would be better for you now. We will have a car waiting for you at Friedrichstrasse Station."

"Tell Herr Glazunov to call me first thing in the morning at the Hilton."

And he hung up.

He reconstructed their conversation for a clue to who she was speaking for, the Germans or the Russians. She had called him "Herr," which indicated that she was probably German, perhaps a good comrade. He did not know the degree of independence allowed the D.D.R. by the U.S.S.R. recently. Come to think of it, there were whole areas in the world he had not followed closely. The networks and now the newspapers they owned as profit centers had turned nations into ten-second headlines and sixty-second stories, following the middle commerical. But he could hardly blame them for his own ignorance; lately, the news itself had somehow seemed unimportant in the old sense of shedding light and causing change.

He called the farm again and told the message recorder to tell its master that he was at the Berlin Hilton overnight and would proceed eastward in the morning.

Before calling it a night, he followed the curve of lights down the Kurfurstendamm and matched the old images from the books and plays and movies with the new realities, and, strangely, it was still Berlin, trying hard and lacking chic, the wide streets reminders of past glory but the residents, smelling musty, seemed a generation behind in their clothing, the old people wearing the last hats of formality as they took their after-dinner stroll in search of yesterday, adorned in ratty-feathered furs that had seen better years in closets, the zonked youngsters doing temporary duty speaking street jive learned from the black occupying army of the night before leaving for work in the west, women painted yellow and violet under the glow of neon lamps just as the sentimental songs commanded, the preoccupation with the next meals in the menus posted outside beer halls and quick-snack bars boasting of pig hocks, roast goose and potato dumplings awash in brown gravy and, on the sidewalks in between, the barkers for the ballhaus and strip clubs with exotic names selling zig-zag for every taste and sex, a main drag of foreign imports trans-shipped through the dreary no-man's-land of the D.D.R., a city whistling in the dark, trying to overlook the fact that the *volk* were surrounded by the Four Powers of a dead war and the neutrons of the next holocaust.

Linkum stopped for a dark creamy beer, said "nein danke" politely to one of Lili Marlene's daughters, and walked slowly up the Ku-damm to Budapesterstrasse. Yes, he thought, the plumbing at the Hilton worked well; the Germans were still good at plumbing. He twirled the dial of the Telefunken on the table next to his bed until he found the Berlin Philharmonic, listened to the clarinet cantilena of Brahms Sonata No. 2 in E-flat Major, and fell asleep with the music on.

The ringing phone was not musical at all.
He reached for his wristwatch: 9 a.m.

"Rise and shine, chum," Chorley said.

"Up yours—you woke me—"

"You have no kick coming—it's the middle of the night for me on this end. Don't you know there's a war on?"

"I'm on overtime. I see you got my message. A little overkill, don't you think? I mean, your people—"

"We can talk about that later. What time are you skedded to make contact with your friend?"

"I'm waiting to hear this morning—I didn't want to make my move until I heard from him directly."

"Drop your cock and get started. There's a little more urgency."

"They ordered me to take the S-Bahn overground to Friedrichstrasse. The old sealed train number. But I want to go through Checkpoint Charlie. I want to walk through the fucking Wall on foot, if I can, because this may be my first and last time in Berlin."

"I'll go along with you on that—good for your soul and any doubts about what we're up to. Anyway, it's better for us if you stay out of trains and cars. We may be able to track you in the open. They'll pick up your scent no matter which way you enter the D.D.R., have no fear. Only thing I want is for you to speed things up. There's something in the air and more pieces coming together."

"I'll see him today if he's there."

"He's there." Chorley sounded as if he was certain. "Good luck, and watch your ass—because they'll be watching it."

Still there was no phone call or message light flickering in his room. He decided to take his chances anyway and cross over. It was raining lightly. He packed his overnight carry-on bag and went downstairs for breakfast, American-style, with burned brown toast instead of applecake with whipped cream. The autocratic doorman wearing the brass buttons of authority tried to get him to say where he was going and to share a cab. He declined. Feeling like a New Yorker bucking the system again, he walked a block to the turning corner before the Hilton and picked off a taxi.

"Zimmerstrasse und Friedrichstrasse," he said.

"Checkpoint Charlie," the driver replied casually.

Linkum asked the old man behind the wheel to drive close to the Reichstag. The brochure said it had been reconstructed, but it looked like a faded postcard from a dead era reborn only for the Sunday rotogravure. In the distance, passing Strasse des 17 Juni, he saw the towering Brandenburger Tor. The triumphal arch loomed like a stage setting for an old movie that would be packed up and crated away. Then, approaching his destination, the streets suddenly appeared half-deserted. Abandoned buildings, pockmarked by artillery shells, became dreary monuments of plaster: a stop-frame of war.

The small outpost was actually called Checkpoint Charlie. Able, Baker, Charlie, Dog: the most unimportant things absorbed in wartime clung to memory. Inside, three bored enlisted men in dress leggings sat reading *The Stars and Stripes* and writing letters home. He walked past their post to the red-and-white, candy-striped barrier and climbed the half-dozen wooden steps erected for visitors who wanted to peer over the Wall

The Wall itself was dumb: a dumb show of silent force, an admission of rule by concrete, barbed wire, shards of glass and tank traps. For a hundred yards on the other side, there were no signs of life. But slogans painted across the factory buildings proclaimed and importuned, glorifying work. He thought: Beware of governments that tell you—as the sign over the gates of Auschwitz did—"Arbeit Macht Frei." The good tyrants took the black humor of the inhuman tyrants of the Third Reich and turned it upside down; they called for work to bring freedom to prove the state worked.

Linkum descended the steps and turned into the maze that marked the official entranceway into East Berlin. The moment he stepped onto their jerrybuilt turf, he sensed an air of disdain. It was as if they were telegraphing a message: We don't have to shape up for you foreigners, like it or lump it, we're superior *volk*. The instructions for passport holders were printed on a piece of cardboard suspended on a string in German, French and English. He pressed the electric buzzer to open the grill gate at the beginning of the game. It shut behind him on a creaky spring. The Iron Curtain didn't need diplomatic bargaining; it needed a can of oil.

Three uniformed women in green skirts and blouses with red piping stood at the far end of a wooden walkway, sipping lemonade and cold tea. He attempted to pass them, smiling; unsmiling, they pointed him toward a door. A tieless official in civilian dress pointed to a sign above his head: Deposit Passport. Doing so, he suddenly felt as if he had become an unperson without identity. He saw a pulley pick up his passport and carry it into the hidden files and stamps of clerkdom. He waited. Now he was on his own. If Chorley's men were tracking him, it would be hard for them inside these wooden boxes. Fifteen, then twenty minutes passed—enough time to reproduce his photograph and the details in his passport. After an hour his name was called, his face scrutinized against the photograph and his passport returned. He moved to the next room and handed over ten dollars for the visa that was good until midnight; for the privilege of entering the Deutsche Demokratische Republik. The next arrow pointed to the room for money exchange. The voiceless sign demanded three more dollars: in return, he was handed tin coins from the D.D.R. "You forgot to say 'please'," he said. Bad joke. The uniform glared back and thumbed him to the next room. His handbag was searched; the film in his camera removed over his protests, then returned, exposed. The dour woman inspector wore a brass caduceus on her green blouse. Maybe this was basket-case duty. Voicelessly, she pointed to the last door in the maze. He stood in front of it until, in her own good time, the woman pressed the electric buzzer. It creaked open and he found himself in the open street, where a sign in three languages declared:

"Welcome to the German Democratic Republic!"

Beneath the sign stood a corporal and a private first-class. Folded Maschinenpistole MP-40's, with foot-long clips, dangled from their shoulders.

Linkum proceeded to walk up Friedrichstrasse. In the shadow of the Brandenburger Tor, the pockmarked buildings were the mirror-image of those on the western side of Checkpoint Charlie. A few men and women in squared suits passed him without a second glance. There was a quiet, disciplined line waiting in front of a store carrying imported foodstuffs from neighboring countries. No children were in sight. Everyone appeared to be shopping. At the corner of Friedrichstrasse a block from Unter den Linden, he spotted a car making a U-turn and then following him slowly. When he reached the wide boulevard, a chauffeur-driven black Moskvich pulled ahead of him and then blocked his path. A voice called out in English:

"Welcome to the D.D.R.!"

Andrei Glazunov stepped out of the limousine and extended his hand. He looked less relaxed.

"Welcome to Mickey Mouse," Linkum replied.

"I think I know what you are referring to," Glazunov said.

"Do you? I mean all the Mickey Mouse I just had to go through at the crossover point—all that junk while they photocopied my passport and made me cool my heels. It's not Venice."

"It's not Moscow either—they are holier than the Pope here, as the old saying goes. You gave the answering service a hard time—I expected you yesterday. My car was waiting for you at the railway crosspoint. We could have had some fun last night."

"Your people wouldn't let me speak with you directly."

Glazunov nodded.

"We're not always neat," he said matter-of-factly.

"Let's go, I have a suite laid on for us at the Unter den Linden Hotel. You've had a hectic morning with the bureaucrats and this drizzle is not good for the bones at our age."

Stepping into the limousine, he looked around casually to see if one of Hap Chorley's people might be nearby. But then he thought better of it; if they were recognizable to him, they wouldn't last long here. If he watched them and was noticed, he wouldn't be watching his ass.

The suite was large—bedrooms on both ends separated by a living room and kitchen. It was decorated in Soviet neo-academic style: colossal combined with asinine.

Glazunov poured two fingers of vodka from a bottle in the freezer. When Linkum declined, he drank his too.

"Now, old friend, have you a present for me?"

Linkum looked around the living room, walked over to the window, and ran his fingers below the ledge. "Is this a convenient place for us to talk?"

Glazunov put his hand to his lips and shook his head. Loudly, he said, "This is one of the finest hotels in East Germany. The management is extremely courteous and efficient. We are among friends here."

Linkum nodded. "That's what I thought. And so artistically decorated too."

Glazunov pointed to the photographic prints of workers with bulging muscles jumping, putting the shot and tossing the javelin. He held his nose and grimaced. "Of course I would be happy to invite you to lunch at the television tower restaurant. From the Telecafe you can get a beautiful panoramic view of the entire city."

But instead of going to the ugly Telecafe tower, Glazunov guided Linkum out of the back of the hotel to Rathausstrasse, then proceeded along a narrow street to Karl-Marx-Allee, where they were lost among the lunchtime strollers. Linkum began to take out his camera from its case. "Put it away," Glazunov ordered. Circling back to Unter den Linden, they passed a ghostly hulk haunted by skinny street cats: Berlin's Main Synagogue, burned down during Crystal Night by the Nazis and burned again during the Allied bombings and now a *Judenrein* monument under the D.D.R.

"Why don't we stop and talk right here?" Glazunov said. "Nobody comes to pay homage to this place."

"I don't see it on the standard itinerary," Linkum said. "But I was hoping that we were heading for the Staatsmuseum."

"That's where they would look for an art curator if we succeeded in shaking them loose after they discovered we were not lunching at the Telecafe."

"And who do you mean—*them*?"

For the first time all morning, Glazunov smiled.

"You know who I mean, Sam. The agents—the busybodies from your side, my side, the German polizei, the Bulgarians, who knows? Even the Arabs have an intelligence operation here, for prestige purposes. They see a Russian and an American together in the bridal suite of a showplace state hotel and everybody is alerted. They report back either rape or détente—both suspicious. The hotel stooges get paid from all sides, even in

157

this well-behaved country. The more they invent, the richer they get."

Glazunov looked out of the corner of his eyes, barely moving his head, but only some old people walked past them.

"Okay—you go first."

"The fat man wants me to tell you two things, Andrei. First, he has heard that there will be a demonstration of your geological weapon very, very soon. Second, that once that occurs, our own weapon will come into play and our efforts—yours and mine—will turn to smoke."

"What is your weapon?"

"I've never been told, Andrei."

"But you have an extra piece of information. What can I trade if you give me nothing?"

"I'm giving your intelligence something very important—and it's something even old warhorses can figure out. If Hap Chorley says that he has heard, it means either a breach in your security or that his listening devices have picked up your preparations. Can I guess which?"

"If it's more than a guess, go ahead."

"Well, I'm sure he hasn't told me anything more than I should know and pass along. But he has spoken of electronic listening devices with very big ears. I know they were sharpened during the testing years in the Vietnam War. Around the Pentagon, they used to say that sensors and computers could tell the difference between

158

a man and an animal coming down the Ho Chi Minh Trail—that they could, I swear, pick up the sounds of elephants fucking a hundred miles away."

"That didn't help your son, Sam."

Linkum flushed. He kept still. Glazunov realized that he had overstepped the bounds by personalizing. "I am being sympathetic, not sarcastic, in my crude way," he said. He touched Linkum's shoulder.

In the rubble of the synagogue, they watched the prowling cats seize and share a thin rat and disappear behind a broken brick wall.

"All right, capitano, here is what I have been told to pass along. There will be a demonstration on a particular day of Soviet strength in a new field. The exact date, I cannot tell you. I have not been told myself. But keep this in mind: If what happens begins precisely at 1100 hours, your people can safely assume that it was no accident of nature. I don't have to put that in writing for you. The exact time and the phrase—no accident of nature—are all you need to remember."

"Anything else—any elaboration?"

Glazunov thought for a moment. "Yes, I am permitted to explain that, under the circumstances, 1100 hours is a time when most people are out of their houses and in the fields or factories. It is a very humanitarian time."

"*Humanitarian?*"

"That is their word, too."

Linkum said, "We destroyed the village in order to save it."

Glazunov said, puzzled, "What does that mean?"

159

"Oh, it was one of the black jokes they used to make after a search-and-destroy operation in Vietnam."

Glazunov nodded. "Well, now we can stroll over to the Staatsmuseum—"

The long Moskvich roared around a corner and screeched to a halt in front of the moribund synagogue. Only the chauffeur, an East German, was in the limousine, sweating. But tailing him openly was an unmarked BMW with two burly customers inside. They parked their car across the street.

"Herr Glazunov, I thought I lost you. I had a message that you wished for me to drive you to the Telecafe."

"*Nein, danke.* My friend and I decided to take a nice walk. The rain has stopped, and the lindens smell so fresh."

"There are no lindens here, Herr Glazunov." The chauffeur looked toward the synagogue's ruins. "Nothing grows in that place—it's just an old dumping-ground. They ought to tear it down, but they say the Jews would make a big propaganda noise again."

"*Mein herr,*" Glazunov said quietly, "it has been destroyed twice in a lifetime already, but in neither case did the Jews do it."

"Well," the German said indifferently, "I would have been in trouble if I had not found you. My orders were to be available at all times. Lucky for me that you did not stray too far."

"*Mein herr,*" Glazunov said. "I do not take orders—

160

from you or your friends across the street. I am a citizen of the Soviet Union. Now, you are dismissed until I call you directly."

The German bowed slightly, looked uneasily at his bosses in the BMW, and drove off.

"That's the first time that I've seen heels clicked except in old Nazi movies," Linkum said, allowing himself a laugh.

"I have dealt with these Krauts before. They are not happy until you snap them to attention. Once in a while they have to be reminded who captured Berlin."

"For a museum curator you're a pretty tough egg," Linkum said, but Glazunov shook his head. "Not so, Sam. It only happens to me when I cross the borders into Germany. I feel like, as you say, kicking ass here."

"I would still like to get to the Staatsmuseum before crossing back myself," Linkum said. "I'm supposed to be writing an article for the art journal, remember? I really would like to see what they have of the Blue Rider school."

"But you must stay overnight. Do not worry about your visa—I can fix that by telephone."

Linkum hesitated, then said, "No, not after what you've told me—I'd better not lose any time."

They walked on to the Staatsmuseum. The thugs followed them at an indiscreet distance, allowing them to move ahead, then gunning their extra-powered BMW to a stop and staring, as if to send a message: We're watching and don't give a damn if you know it. Linkum wondered: Are they watching Andrei, not me, and if so,

161

are their contractors the East Germans or the Russians?

In a wing on the second floor of the museum there were a sprinkling of works by Kandinsky, Marc, Kubin and Munter.

"They're weak on Klee," Glazunov said. "The best Blue Rider collection is in the Stadtische Galerie in Munich, anyway."

"If we make it, I'd like to go there with you someday," Linkum said.

"It's a deal," Glazunov said, shaking Linkum's hand, then added, "Cheer up, when you get to the Hermitage I'll show you one of our Picassos with the same blue in it that Kandinsky and Marc loved."

They bought some postcards of museum reproductions on the way out. The students they had seen in the museum looked utterly different from the muscular Nordics pictured on the D.D.R. sports posters. Several wore the very same anti-nuclear war buttons Linkum had noticed on jackets of the young people strolling on the Kurfurstendamnn: ATOMKRAFT? NEIN DANKE!

As they reentered the Unter den Linden, Glazunov paused at the hotel entranceway. Turning to the tailing BMW, he slapped his arm and raised his fist defiantly toward the two occupants. "I wanted to see if they know the sign language for *up your ass* in Italian," and Linkum said, "It's universal."

In the hotel suite, Linkum examined his handbag. "My turn," he said aloud. "They went through it." "Welcome to the D.D.R. Did they take anything?" "A book. I managed to get it through Checkpoint

Charlie but they were so busy pulling the film out of my camera that they overlooked it."

"What was the title?"

"It was just a little paperback by Wolf Biermann called *The Wire Harp*—the East German balladeer they kicked out because his lyrics ridiculed the nonsense of the regime."

"Rubbing it in—what could you expect?"

"I expected that my stuff would be left alone."

"Well, that's one you can't blame on the Russians, Sam. Obviously, the local polizei did not want a Biermann book here." He spoke as if addressing an audience through a microphone. "Ridicule is not permitted under socialism, and you were a bad boy."

Linkum glanced at his watch. If he got through Checkpoint Charlie quickly, there would be time to pick up his luggage at the Berlin Hilton and just catch the trans-Atlantic flight out of Frankfurt.

"Leave it to me," Glazunov said.

He called a number and spoke quickly in Russian. Then he summoned the Moskvich; the chauffeur forced a sullen smile.

At the Checkpoint, a Soviet Embassy official greeted them and walked over to an East German colonel near the barrier.

"No Mickey Mouse this time," Glazunov said, smiling. "You are cleared through."

They had a moment alone.

"I hope to see you soon—if you're still talking to

me," Glazunov said.

"Listen, Andrei," Linkum said. "There's your side, and there's my side. But you're you, and I'm still me."

By The Associated Press.

ISTANBUL, Turkey—A major earthquake ripped open the Anatolia Fault in eastern Turkey today, leaving 3,000 dead and at least 2,000 missing, according to official Government sources.

The Kandilli Observatory in Istanbul reported that the quake had a magnitude of 6.9 on the Richter scale. The epicenter of the upheaval—in a seismic region of eruptions in the earth's crust since at least the Minoan civilization perished in 1450 B.C.—is between Lake Van and Mount Ararat, where the Old Testament alleges that Noah's Ark came to rest.

"The death toll could have been much worse," a Defense Ministry spokesman declared. "God willed it that the tremor occurred at a time when most of the villagers were working outside in the fields. Many of the victims were women and children who perished in their mud-brick houses. All possible assistance is being rushed to Anatolia by the Red Crescent, with the full cooperation of the Turkish Army and North Atlantic Treaty Organization medical evacuation forces."

The quake struck at 11 A.M. (4 A.M. New York time), sending shock waves for over 200 miles—up to the borders of Iran and Soviet Armenia.

Six

"**W**ELL, THEY'VE screwed the heathen—and us at the same time," Hap Chorley said.

"But I still can't figure out why they did it while Andrei was still negotiating with us," Sam Linkum said. "Do you think he knew the green light was on for the mission all the time we were talking?"

The director of USAFSS watched his cigar smoke perform a half-Immelmann in the clouds over his Pentagon desk.

Linkum waited for his reaction; to his own surprise, he also found himself hoping for a word of approval.

"I wouldn't call it a negotiation, chum. I'd call it a rout—and a warning." Chorley put his feet up. "Several warnings, in fact, according to what we've picked up through ELINT."

"Do you think there was something I could have done—or Andrei—to prevent their test demonstration?"

"Our analysis is that Glazunov knew some stuff but

on the operation itself, he didn't know shit from Shinola. Is that your impression too?"

"I'd like to think that he told me what he knew. If not, he's the best damn liar in the Soviet Union. He knew it was going to happen, and he passed on the precise time. That, at least, was accurate. They could have prevented me from getting back through Checkpoint Charlie. He made a tentative effort, trying to get me to stay with him at the Unter den Linden, but he didn't press it when I said I wanted to get back fast to Washington. That indicates to me—"

"If it's any consolation to you," Chorley interrupted, "my sources tell me that he got his ass reamed for not keeping you there longer. Not that either of you could have influenced the operational date. It's been in the works for fifteen months. Glazunov was pissed at the KGB, I hear, when he got back to Moscow and read about it in *Pravda*."

"I read about it on the flight home in the *International Herald Trib*. Frankly, I thought you'd chew me out."

"Sambo, you did all right."

It was the first kind word that Linkum had received from Chorley since his return; and he found himself pleased, and at the same time disturbed that he was pleased, at the mild professional praise.

"Why the hell couldn't they have picked some remote place to test their seismic weapon?" Linkum said. "Why kill a lot of innocent people who aren't their enemy even theoretically?"

"Because they don't give a shit about the peasants—

even when they call them the proletariat. When they get through adding up the corpses under the rubble, the death toll will reach ten thousand."

"What a horrible warning—if the Turks understood it. It's a cold-blooded murder."

"They don't understand it—that's the beauty of the seismic weapon. And we can't tell them. But I'm going to tell you something you're not supposed to know, old cock. It wasn't a warning, it was an act of war. Americans died in that rubble too—including some of my men. Ten thousand Turks were just a secondary target of opportunity against our eastern end of NATO."

Linkum said, "What was the primary target?"

"Me. Us. The U. S. of A. The deaths were regrettable. But the real loss was something else—my listening-post in Anatolia. The fuckers took it out."

Linkum nodded; and he thought to himself: I'd rather not share Hap Chorley's USAFSS eyes-only, burn-bag secrets, I'm being sucked into more than I bargained for.

"We had a lot of sophisticated equipment up there in the mountains," Chorley continued. "Sure, sensors don't bleed, but it took a lot of money and wheeling-and-dealing to get my electronic intelligence in place. It worked almost as well as direct aerial surveillance. We paid our esteemed Turkish ally a ton of baksheesh—something in the neighborhood of fifty million in surplus aircraft for them to crash in training and another fifty million under the table to bribe the generals in Ankara and the provincial officials in Anatolia. I was two hundred miles closer to the Motherland than the CIA setup on the Black Sea. Now all I've got is a bunch of relics and a red face."

Linkum said, "What about your men? Did you really take casualties?"

Hap Chorley accidentally kicked over his seventy-five millimeter ashtray.

"Four, maybe five, college professors," he said. "Our front was an archeological dig. I had some of the same professors that I used under contract during the Vietnam War. Their universities, by the way, were happy to cooperate and serve as the conduit for payments. You know, you can most always buy a professor by dangling a fat research grant, a conference at the Aspen Institute in Colorado or Berlin, and a guarantee that you'll get his book published afterward, never mind how."

"I thought only the CIA was in the book publishing business," Linkum said. "My paper exposed them a long time ago."

"There's more than one way to get around you wiseass journalists. Such as putting in an order in advance for a couple thousand books at fifteen or twenty dollars a copy that nobody's going to read, not even in the American libraries overseas. Anyway, my professors were supposedly looking for the umpteenth Lion Gate of the Hittites. They turned up what must have been the most expensive rocks in the world. On the side, they dug up the real stuff—analyzing electronic data about the Russkies in Soviet Armenia."

"Where do you think Andrei stands now in all this?" Linkum wondered. "Is he still effective?"

Chorley shrugged. "If they need him, he'll be there. But I know where my friend Madame Zaremba stands after loosening up the earth plates by remote control in the Anatolia Fault—damn high. She could make it all the way to the Politburo for pulling it off. And I look like a shithead. I had to tell the Air Force Chief of Staff, and he personally told the President."

"That's the way they did it—by remote control."

"Oh, it's a lot more complicated than merely pushing a button. So far they have to be within five hundred miles of the epicenter. But that could be refined. We're talking about people who could mobilize enough resources to beat us into space. Setting off a quake is precision work coordinating weather, time and vulnerability. And then they need mapping that's good to the last centimeter. Like our Geodetic Survey maps. We're dumb enough to sell them through our Government Printing Office—giving them our earth plates on a silver platter. But it's not just technology that counts, it's moxie—the cold-assed cool to be willing to wipe out a hundred villages like blowing out this matchstick. That's the real advantage they have over most of us—"

"They can have it, Hap. Otherwise, we're them."

"You might think otherwise one of these days."

"I don't think so. In my racket—when I had a real job—I had to be cynical sometimes to stay in business. Especially when I was dealing with government officials. That was the training. I don't think I was conned too often."

Chorley walked over to his Arlington window,

picked up his field glasses, and swept them around the Washington landmarks.

Then he turned quickly. "I'll ask you again, Sam, when they target a point in the Continental United States."

The intercom blinked on Chorley's desk.

"You carry it yourself, Maryjane," he said softly.

She teetered in, shook her long mane, and dropped a coded dispatch in Chorley's hand. He held hers for a moment.

"Thank you, honey," he said, watching her balancing act on spiked heels.

"The Greeks had a word for it," Linkum said, studying her haunches. "A callipygian vision."

"She's just a down-home girl who doesn't need fancy words. I bet she'd appreciate it if you just said, What an ass."

Chorley took a pocket decoder from the locked side of his desk and punched the keys for several minutes.

"Speaking of the devil," he said, "you may get your chance to see General Zaremba yet."

He ran his thick index finger over the decoded notes.

"ELINT has picked up that your invitation to the Hermitage is going to be renewed formally."

Linkum said, "That means Andrei is still my opposite number in this game of show-and-tell."

"Well, put it that he keeps his amateur standing—like you. Do you still have that color postcard of the Antonello Madonna from the Palermo museum?"

Linkum reached inside his jacket pocket and held it up.

"Because our Bulgarian hard-on should be making contact with you in a day or two."

"Why would they want me? Why not you—directly?"

"I'm too visible. Too many correspondents would report my presence. That's one nice thing about the Moscow press—they know what not to print on security matters."

"How would you like to be the American newspaper censor?"

Chorley laughed. "No, thank you." He thought for a moment and said, "The only time I get to Moscow is on official business that they know and we know are authorized coverups: the international air shows. There's usually some phony celebration of VE-Day or the meeting at the Elbe. Of course, neither one of us shows his advanced aircraft there or in the big Paris flyby, but these things are worth attending just to see how good their pilots are—and they're pretty hot shit. Who the hell knows? With their seismic weapon, some of us won't need our wings."

"I still don't know how or why I figure in the new equation."

"Because they want to get a reading on what they pulled off and what our reaction is. Especially, on our countermeasure—where, when, and if we're going to hit back in kind."

"How much will I be able to tell Andrei this time?

I didn't have much to trade, and I don't want Andrei to think I'm holding back—"

"You'll have more than you can imagine."

"Will it involve deaths like the Anatolia thing?"

"Well, let me just say, not directly. If that makes you feel better. But you'll find out soon enough."

Linkum nodded, knowing it would be futile to press for details now.

"Hap, I've got a small personal problem. I think you know what it is."

Chorley replied, "Okay, you can see her."

Linkum smiled. "Thank you."

"I leave it to your discretion about how much to say. I've checked—no, don't worry, very quietly. She's doing fine on the job. And I've also been following her stuff in the paper. She's a helluva writer—simple and clear."

"That's half the battle when you're putting a piece together. The other half she's also got—having something to say because of who you are and what you stand for."

"Some day, if all this turns out to be a bum dream, I'd like to meet her," Chorley said. Then he stood up and placed his hand on Linkum's shoulder. "I want you back at my farm in two days, ready to move east, and fast."

Just below her left shoulder blade, almost beyond self-touch, Jennie Ives had a four-inch scar that she found embarrassing. She chose her beachwear and blouses carefully to conceal it. The first time they had been together, flesh to flesh in the bedroom dark, Sam Linkum had inadvertently come on the scar. . . . He ran

172

his fingers along its length. Her body shivered at his touch, the spell of passion was broken and she flicked on the bedside lamp. He wondered if, somehow, he had offended her sensibilities. She stood up naked in front of him, turned around to reveal her back, and, looking over her shoulder with a shy smile, said:

"It's still me."

With her beautifully veined hand, she reached up to show him the scar in the light.

"I suppose it requires an explanation," she said.

The gash had raised a welt in her skin and lightened the flesh tone. It looked as if it had taken a long time to heal.

"Not if you don't feel like it," Sam said.

"I do—with you."

"Come here a moment," he said, reaching for her hand.

Then he, too, stood up. Holding her around the waist, he brushed his lips along the scar and kissed it, slowly and deliberately.

"All better," he said.

Tears filled her eyes, and she cried softly.

They stared at each other, without talking.

Then she said, "I must look like a raccoon, with my mascara running," and he said, "No, more like a chipmunk."

She poked him playfully and said, "Thanks a bunch," and went to the bathroom to wipe her face.

"You look like a little girl, without makeup," he said. "I love your face, Jennie."

They sat up in her bed together, arms around one another, like friends.

"It happened twelve years ago, long before we first met. I was engaged to someone I thought was wonderful. He was, in his way. A brilliant student, with a master's in astronomy. We had known each other in graduate school, when I was an English major. Chaucer, would you believe it? *She was a worthy woman all her life, husbands at church door she had five.* I still remember whole chunks of *The Canterbury Tales.* Anyway, we met again in Ecuador. Without knowing it, we had both signed up for the Peace Corps and wound up in the same place. I was teaching nursing—it was really more like first aid—after a crash course at Bellevue, and he was teaching basketball. They love basketball there, and it became part of a general health program. At night we'd look at the heavens and he would point out the constellations. It was a romantic time for us, and maybe for feelings about the United States too. Then, something happened—a little thing. We were drinking the local brew with some of the other Peace Corps people. A few of us got up and danced, just imitating the fancy steps we had seen in an old Astaire movie the night before at the compound, but he didn't. He was a lousy dancer, awkward and athletic. I saw him watching me, and then he suddenly yanked me away from the guy I was waltzing with. When we got home, he threw a punch. When he tried to touch me in bed I wouldn't make love. I put it out of mind, blaming the brew, until he hit me again a month later. I began to wonder a lot about his mean streak. Then I got pregnant and decided not to have the child. He was very pleased with himself about my pregnancy. He even offered to marry me right away. Instead, I had an abortion. When he found out that I had gone through with it—and it wasn't very pleasant—he took it as a deliberate affront to his manhood, or something. He came swinging at me with the first thing he grabbed, a tin sculpture of a mythical bird that I'd bought in the Indian marketplace. I turned to run but he caught me in the back with it. He walked away, leaving me bleeding. I went to the hospital for the second time in two days to be patched up. With a lot of blood and tears. End of story. Not very pretty, I'm afraid."

"God," Linkum said, "what a son-of-a-bitch he must have been."

"Who knows what he was or what was bugging him at the time. He came around a couple of days later, very contrite, after I'd moved out of our place. I managed enough strength to tell him what I had been rehearsing to say if I ever saw him again—that I could never have a child with someone I didn't love."

"What happened after that?"

"I was drummed out of the Peace Corps," she said, smiling. "No, not quite. Actually, I decided to quit because it was too uncomfortable being in the same town, with the same small circle of gossip, and the same routine of getting blasted on local brew every other night. My FBI file must show somewhere that I got an F in Peace Corps and let our country down. What the hell—"

"Did you ever see the guy again?"

"No, and I didn't want to. I've never told the whole story to anyone but you. One of my friends ran into him

175

in Oregon. Said he was coaching a high school basketball team and teaching astronomy on the side. I'm sure he's very good at both."

Linkum said, "It's infuriating to think it happened to you. And I admit I feel sort of jealous, even if it was a long time ago."

"My God, not jealous. Neither he nor anyone else comes close to you. To us. We inhabit another planet. You know that, Sam. What I do think about is that pregnancy. I might have had a child who would have been a teen-ager by now. But I'm past the safe age, and it's too late. All I've got left from that affair is a gash."

He ran his fingers along her back, tenderly. She shivered beneath his hand, and lowered her eyes. They were swollen with tears.

"Thank you for telling me," he said. "Most people have a scar somewhere. Yours just happens to be on the outside." . . .

Now they were together again in her apartment in Gramercy Park as if nothing had occurred in the last few weeks to change the familiar intimacies.

"I've missed you terribly," Jennie said. "I almost wore out your picture looking at it so much."

"I left the small black-and-white passport picture of you home but I carried your face and body in my head."

"I'm better in living color—"

"Better in the flesh," he said.

"Just keep holding me, Sam darling."

"Lie down on top of me so I can feel all of you closer."

She rolled over. "It makes every nerve in my body

go to sleep this way. You're medicine, my special pre-
scription."

After a moment he said, "This is the good part of
being away."

He had not told her very much till now. When he
rang, she had not questioned him about the missing days.

"I mean, the coming back part. Knowing you'll be
here and invite me in for a sleepover date. Knowing my
robe is hanging in your closet."

But her very lack of questioning was more than
politeness; it made the lack significant.

"I've brought you a little present," he whispered.

He reached over and took a small package from the
pocket of his robe. She unwrapped it carefully and held
the carved wooden angel under the bedside light.

"A seraph . . . how did you know I've always
wanted one?"

"Because you're an angel." He laughed. "You gave
an old romantic a perfect lead-in line."

"Thank you, but I'm afraid you don't know your
order of angels. I'm more of your fat cherub. This one
is a real seraph. The genuine article has three pairs of
wings."

"I never even noticed."

"Elementary angelology, old chap. Seraphs are very
high in the order of celestial messengers."

"I must have had you in mind when I picked it out."

She twirled the figure on its string, circling it over
his head.

"It's handcarved," he said. "Sicilian."

"I haven't seen one like this before. They're usually

made of plastic painted over with rosy touches. If you stole it in a church, don't tell me."

"I got it in a woodcarver's shop in Palermo."

She stopped the dancing seraph.

"Oh . . ."

Jennie placed her present on the night table.

Sam hesitated for a moment, preparing his half-truth. Then he said cheerfully, "A quickie assignment to cover an art thing in the old country for my friend's magazine. You've met him." She nodded. "It was a way to make a few bucks and get away from the Lifestyles scene."

"I was concerned about you—concerned, darling, not worried. I wish you had phoned so I could have heard your voice."

"I heard yours."

"What? . . . Oh, well. I *thought* it might have been you calling from abroad, but the line went dead. Well, you bum, at least you heard me say hello. I didn't even get a postcard."

But even a postcard, he knew, could be telling in his new line of work for USAFSS.

"I thought it would be better to leave you alone. Let you fly solo with the new management. As far as they're concerned, I'm last year's hotel. Delafield probably has her own people on the premises already, spying on the staff. I'm afraid that if word got back to her that we were seen together, your reputation would be on the line—"

"How do you mean that?" she broke in.

"Reputation may be the wrong word. I meant professionally—that your job might be in trouble.

There's a green-eyed monster curled up inside Delafield's head. She could never find fault with your work. When it comes to editing or writing—what the honchos at the network call *communications*—you're way up here and she's down there. But if you were known as a Linkum loyalist, she'd try to zap you."

"That's better," Jennie said. "For a minute, I thought you were trying to say something about our relationship."

He took her cheeks between his hands and looked at her directly.

"We're us. The two of us. Nothing comes between us."

She moved his hands to her lips. He kissed her forehead.

After a while he asked her about how she was surviving and if the cut list had been put into effect. Strangely, she said, no one in her little area had been fired but otherwise bodies were falling all over the place. That's the way they put it: bodies. Some of the news people were given the option of shaping up or shipping out to the affiliates halfway across the country to beef up (their phrase) the news operations in places in Alabama or Oklahoma or a dozen other nowheresvilles away from the big time. It turned out to be the start of a campaign to bust the dwindling power of the newspaper unions. The network lawyers insisted that the bodies could be moved anywhere under the contracts; it was transfer or deal yourself out. Most of the writers had chosen to take their severance pay and risk it in the big new electronic world that was turning news into product for the cable and cassettes.

"What news?" Sam said. "Redefine your terms. You mean *software*, don't you? I think that's become my favorite word to despise," he said.

"They own the bats and balls and playing fields," Jennie said. "There's no other way of reaching the big numbers now that the networks control the papers. Oh, there's still *The Nation* and *The Progressive*, but it's a good idea to use a pseudonym. What do you think my byline was in *The Nation*?"

"Delafield spelled backwards?"

"Not even close, Sam. Brett, as in Lady Brett, that silly romantic Hemingway character I've always loved: slightly promiscuous and, somewhere in the depths of her heart, unattainable. Brett Ashley, but thank heavens, you're not Jake Barnes." She touched him playfully.

"And I can prove it," he said.

And he did.

In the morning he put up the coffee and brought hers in bed.

The newspaper—there was only one left in the morning field in New York—lay curled outside her door, its sections scattered, and she brought them to him. He turned to the daily *Lifestyles* section, glancing at the headlines and running his eyes down the stories to see which public relations agencies were behind them. He generally could spot a planted piece after a couple of paragraphs.

"I'm sorry to say your predictions didn't take too

180

long to come true," Jennie said. "The paper's become mostly gossip columns in disguise and plugs for show business moguls and young executives on the corporate rise."

He glanced at the pages and tossed them away. "They don't seem to make much of an effort to hide the sell-out stuff. At least when we put in a publisher must-run, we tried to disguise it a little."

"Some new geniuses have moved over from the network to show us the light. And they've hired some new writers from the gossip-as-news magazines. Ambitious little ass-kissers who stand for not much of anything except their own careers. Hey, Sam, am I being unfair? Were we that way once?"

"I'd like to think we weren't. We were naive enough to believe that words counted—that tough stories could move mountains. Dammit, every once in a while we *did* shake them up in the Statehouse and even in the White House."

"I wanted to hear you say it," Jennie said. "I don't want to sound like some damn prig, but I swear, some of this new bunch they've brought in can be had for a free lunch at the Four Seasons."

"Careerists—and I'm afraid that's become a dirty word," he said . . . "Have you got a copy of Brett Ashley's piece?"

After reading her story in *The Nation*, he said, "They couldn't have appreciated this on the Avenue of the Americas. I hope that Delafield doesn't try to trace it. You'd last as long as it took her to get you canned. By the way, have I told you this morning that I love you?"

They reached across the kitchen table for each other's hands.

There was a farewell touch in his fingers, but she would not let him go. The parting always hurt; always seemed wrong.

Suddenly she said, "Would you let me go with you today, Sam?"

She had never asked before. He looked at her, surprised, not saying anything; not knowing what to say.

The Thornhill Residence and the military cemetery at Farmingdale were his private domain. No one had ever invaded it, and he had never shared his almost-weekly visits with his closest friends. They knew where he went and respected his aloneness. Jennie, especially, had no part of his past of despair and mourning for the living and dead. He had no desire to mix the two worlds. She was his future: a gift of love he wanted to go on forever without the reminder that he was encumbered.

"I won't be in your way," Jennie persisted after his silence, "but of course maybe I shouldn't have asked at all."

"No, it's not that. You just caught me by surprise. I'd never thought you wanted to go with me. I would have been embarrassed to ask you. I didn't think you. . . ."

His voice trailed off.

"It's just that I can't bear being away from you all day. It seems like such a waste—especially after we've spent the night together. I hate to see the sun come up."

She brushed her hand across his cheek. "I'm sorry, if you'd rather—"

"I'd rather," Sam said gently.

She nodded, smiling to conceal her disappointment.

"I have to keep the different parts of me in different boxes. At least until I get myself straightened out and know where I'm heading."

She looked puzzled, and he said, "I may have to follow up an assignment in Washington. I'll see you in a few days, if not before."

"You know where I'll be," she said. "Waiting." She forced a smile again. "Right here."

"Save my place," he said lightly.

Then he dressed and quickly departed.

Linkum walked to the car rental place near the East River a little north of the United Nations complex. He looked toward the outlines of the Secretariat and Assembly that had once symbolized a chance for peace but, between small wars and colonel-run revolutions, somehow had turned into another bureaucracy dominated by the second-string diplomats of the Third World countries. Nearly two hundred flags snapped in the wind around Barbara Hepworth's monumental sculpture; ironically, the more flags the less effectual the organization. In one generation, the buildings had lost much of their meaning in the smoky New York skyscape.

As he drove up a wind was blowing in from the Sound that rattled the shutters of the Thornhill Residence. The weather and the seasons no longer changed for Elena; he hoped there was someone around who put warm clothing on the patients when they were allowed to go outside. Sometimes, he found her shivering, alone.

"Relative?" the hall nurse asked matter-of-factly, and he replied, "No, husband."

There was a flicker of recognition, no more, as Elena glanced at him in her room. He asked her if she wanted to take a walk, or go for a ride, as he had done during every visit. She remained silent. They sat side-by-side for a few moments, and he held her limp hand.

The rain punctuated the waters in front of Elena's window. He checked the grating to see that it was intact. Ritual; he had done so many times, fearing for her safety. On rainy days, the patients were not permitted to go out with their families, not even their husbands or wives. It was a rule, made more for the convenience of the Residence staff. Linkum looked at his watch. He went down to the car and gathered up the picture magazines that Elena, according to the nurses, looked at occasionally. He placed them in her lap, and turned the pages slowly for her, stopping to read aloud. In his imagination he saw a smile around her lips. Then he placed her carefully in the chair alongside her bed, kissed her forehead, and left her room.

Sam Linkum stepped out of the Residence; out of his guilt-ridden box. He thought: in the morning I embraced Jennie, in the afternoon I touched my lips to Elena. He lived in a small world of departures.

As he started for the car, the hall nurse handed him a telephone message. "Whoever it was said it was urgent," she told him, "but he wouldn't leave a phone number. He sounded long distance."

In the car, he opened the message and read it under an overhead map light: URGENT CALL MARYLAND FARM. Nothing else.

There was no private telephone booth around. He drove through the slashing rain down the middle of Long Island to the cemetery at Farmingdale. He remembered that in the reception area labeled "Next of Kin" there were public phones.

He dialed Hap Chorley, collect.

"Is there anyone in your line of sight? Anyone tailing you?"

Linkum told him that he was phoning on U.S. military grounds and that it was raining like hell outside and there wasn't a Russian agent in sight.

"Take another look," Chorley said impatiently. "I've sent out one of my people to pick you up. Blue Mercury, no markings." Sarcasm roughed the edges of his voice. "You should have spotted him, Sam, just to keep in practice. My people have been with you for hours."

Linkum peered through the glass door into the rain mist. A blue sedan had pulled alongside his rental. In the front seat he saw the outlines of two figures.

"What the hell is so urgent that you had to have your damn spooks interfere with my personal—"

"You'll find out soon enough. But don't call my men spooks, Sam. That's unfair. They're as dedicated as we are, or at least some of us are, in our work."

"But I told you from the start, Hap, that my private life and the mission were two different things. You said you'd respect that."

"And I do. But something's come up very suddenly and I wanted to make sure that you'd get to the farm. Tonight."

One of the figures emerged from the Mercury and made a run for it through the downpour. He shook himself off and stood rigidly at half-attention only a few feet from the phone booth, as if waiting to make a call.

"I've got a jet trainer standing by at MacArthur Airport for you. Shoot you down my way in an hour," Chorley said.

Linkum counted his choices; he had none.

As he stepped out of the booth, the captain saluted him. No pretense now.

"I'm your pilot, sir," the captain said, extending his hand. "Call me Hector."

"Is that your first or your last name?"

"Both," he said, grinning.

"I guess I don't have to introduce myself."

"No sir, Mr. Linkum," the captain said. "Have you got the keys to your car? My friend here will drive it to the city and turn it back." Linkum fished in his pocket and handed over the keys. "You can come with me, sir."

Hap Chorley thought of everything, almost.

Linkum began to walk toward the blue Mercury, then stopped.

"You'll just have to wait for a few moments, Hector," he said when the captain started to follow him. "I won't run away. Sit in your car and stay out of the rain."

The gravesites loomed in long, endless rows. In the Next of Kin room someone had begun to turn off the lights. Linkum headed for the familiar pathway; the long-remembered row and number.

But the gates were closed and the crosses and Stars of David were chained in for the night. There was a thunderclap and, for an instant, a bolt of lightning cast an eery red glow over the section where Antonio was buried. Linkum stood bareheaded under the thunderstorm. He gripped the chain fence in his hands, and peered toward the gravesite until the water running down his eyes and cheeks blurred his vision.

The jet trainer flew above the weather and in less than an hour touched down at Andrews Air Force Base. The raised snouts of a squadron of fighters stood in revetments like prehistoric beasts sniffing the wind. A two-man chopper was parked at the end of the taxi run, and he was rushed into the piggyback seat. Nobody said a word or was expected to; all the signals to him came through deliberate pressure against his elbows. This close to the beltway ringing the District of Columbia; and yet Linkum sensed that he had penetrated some strange arena where masked men, with snakelike air hoses and arteries of electric circuitry coursing through their bodies, stood by waiting for the command to scramble. It was a secretive world of friendly and hostile blips: so the world was divided on the radar screens on both sides. He was a shuttle man himself, LaGuardia to National Airport, National to LaGuardia, same day and home for dinner. But on these runways only a few miles from the winding, peaceful Potomac, Air Force Generals played out scenarios that sent intercontinental ballistic missiles flying to predesignated targets across the heavens.

The chopper fluttered above Hap Chorley's farm, suddenly illuminated by landing-lights that were quickly turned off the moment the plane squatted down on Chorley's backyard landing-pad. Only seconds after Linkum hopped out, the chopper pilot speeded up the whirling blades and lifted off; banking over the treetops, the chopper disappeared across the Maryland hills.

Through the semi-darkness Chorley's voice boomed:

"How do you like my little Air Corps?"

Linkum searched for the direction of the voice.

"The way those landing-lights went on and off, I thought that we were back making a supply drop to the partisans."

Chorley emerged from the shadows and put his thick arm around Linkum.

"Sorry to bust in on your private time, Sam, but this one isn't my show. We're both going to be bystanders— or observers, to be more precise. We've got time for one quick drink before we both get airborne." Chorley filled two tumblers halfway with black label Jack Daniel's. He sipped his seriously, neat; Linkum added a splash of tap water.

"Here's the gen. You and I are about to see an experiment that could be as history-making as Alamogordo before Big Boy was dropped the first time on our now good friends, the Japanese. Only this time it's not supposed to be a nuclear test. No fireball, no radiation, just something neat and clean. The Chemical Warfare boys are proud as hell of what they've got in store for us."

Chorley checked his chronometer that told the time in Washington and Moscow.

"I've got some dry clothes laid out for you. I hope the size is right. There wasn't a chance to go shopping, chum." He downed the rest of his Jack Daniel's in one gulp. "If you can't finish your drink, I'll take along a flask. But we've got to haul ass. In just forty minutes, we're going to be airborne out of Andrews, heading west."

Through the night air, Linkum heard the alien whirr of a propellor.

Chorley raised the window in the living room and looked outside. Then he flicked a switch, and a green circle of lights illuminated his backyard landing-pad. Hector's chopper came down and made room for a second that soon fluttered to earth. Chorley and Linkum climbed into the back seats and the helicopters took off. Below them, the landing-pad lights disappeared into darkness.

At Andrews, an Air Force medium bomber was revving up at the end of the runway. Chorley and Linkum climbed aboard. The plane was fitted with sleeping berths, carpeting, and a galley. They sat down in adjoining upholstered chairs. Nobody else was in the cabin.

"How do you like my private Air Force One?" Chorley said. "Not bad for an old Sicilian."

"Rank has its privileges."

"Especially civilian rank. Otherwise, it would be channels and chickenshit all the way."

He picked up the intercom to the flight deck.

"You may proceed on schedule, colonel," he ordered the pilot. "What's your time now and your E.T.A.? Any problems?" Chorley checked his chronometer. "Contact," he said. The bomber moved into position on the flight line, its engines screamed for sixty seconds, and suddenly they were airborne and above the clouds and weather.

Now Linkum looked at his watch. It was well past midnight of a very long day.

"I'd suggest that you do what I'm going to do for the next three hours—conk out," Chorley said. "Because we're both going to have to be on total alert to what's going on at dawn."

"My engine's still running," Linkum said. "That flask will help to slow it down and put me to sleep." Chorley handed him the rest of his drink and refilled his own from the bar in the galley.

"Wake me when the war's over," Linkum said, closing his eyes.

"Yeah," Chorley said. "I'll do that."

The bomber droned westward.

Linkum felt that he had barely shut his eyes when he felt someone shaking him.

"Okay," Chorley said. "Drop your cocks—"

"—and grab your socks," he groggily finished the old refrain.

Chorley placed a cup of steaming coffee in his hand.

Linkum looked out the window of the aircraft. In the openings of the clouds, he saw mountain peaks covered with snow. They seemed to be flying low; that, or the peaks were high enough to hold snow and ice in the late spring.

"Where are we? The Apennines or the Alps? I thought we were flying westward—"

"Washington."

"Did we turn back?"

"Washington, State of," Chorley said matter-of-factly.

The bomber was banking, beginning its descent. A necklace of glistening lakes and rivers encircled the snow-fringed mountains. Not a town was visible below, and the whole area seemed unpopulated and denuded. Through a pass between the peaks a landing field appeared in the dawn light. Two other aircraft were already on the ground when the Air Force bomber landed. Linkum noticed that the field was surrounded by a double row of chained fencing topped by barbed wire.

Chorley pointed to the parked airplanes and said, "My opposite numbers are already here—the general and admiral heading up the Army Security Agency and the Navy Security Group. One of them's an asshole, I won't say which. The three of us were allowed to bring along only one other staff man from our office. A top aide to share the data and compare impressions."

"Who's yours?"

"You," Chorley told him.

Linkum looked more puzzled than flattered.

"You can count on the fingers of one hand the number of people who know about this experiment—and that includes the President. The technicians themselves only know bits and pieces. But I brought you along so that, when the time comes, you can be our message-bearer to the Kremlin. No, you don't have to storm the walls. Your job is to describe what you see to Capitano Glazunov, he'll tell the KGB, and the ball will be in their court."

"Can you tell me a little more about it?"

"You'll see for yourself. And, Sam, no notes, no speaking to anyone we run into in this area. They're not supposed to ask for or share information—including your name. Especially your name. We're all on our own. This is as secret a show as anything we ever did under wartime conditions. You're a reporter, right? Just put into your memory box what counts and into your forget-tery what doesn't."

A forest-green Land-Rover was parked behind the Operations building. A set of keys dangled from the ignition. There was no driver around; more security.

"Do you know how to shift one of these things?" Chorley said. "I hope you've paid your life-insurance premiums. I took my first instructions on the Land-Rover yesterday. Anyway, climb in—we're heading for the next-to-last roundup."

He shifted into the low gear, and the vehicle rumbled forward, then picked up speed. Chorley drove confidently for about five miles along a dusty, churned-up road. Not once did they pass another car or even a sign. It seemed to be government forest land. The only movement they observed were startled jackrabbits skittering across the road. Every few minutes Chorley glanced at a small map of the region but he kept it—deliberately—on his left side, hidden from view.

"I'm glad one of us isn't lost," Linkum said.

"Sorry, but the specific places where we're heading aren't on your agenda. I've never been here myself, but the directions are accurate and the landmarks on target, so far. We should be hitting our lake any time now."

The rising sun began to cast a fiery glow over the high, rocky banks. Before them lay a still narrower roadway, not more than a tire-treaded path. It was protected by shrubs and exposed, tangled roots. The pathway circled a shimmering lake that seemed to be two, perhaps three miles from any vantage point. Now the sun streaked the lake in a golden, hazy line. Dark fir trees, sentinels that nature had placed here in disciplined rows, stood outlined against the sky, providing a sealed-in intimacy for the hidden lake.

Chorley caused the Land-Rover to crawl in the treaded pathway, and both men studied the scene, knowing memory was part of the assignment. At one break in the road, the waters lapped gently along the edges of the undisturbed forestland. Wild animals could come here unmolested. The clear lake could reflect to the bottom. Flies were hatching beneath the overhanging branches. Suddenly, they noticed movement: a leap of trout with spotted fins and blush-pink stripes, dancing boldly on their tails over the surface, breaking through the pearly waters as if they owned them.

"Breakfast of champions," Chorley said, admiring the trout as they boldly fed in this no-man's-land.

A forest ranger's observation post stood above the treeline, already occupied by the army and navy intelligence chiefs and their aides. All were dressed in disguised mufti except for their giveaway Pentagon PX boots. Chorley and Linkum climbed the wooden staircase and took their places, facing the lake. No one did more than nod; as if acknowledging each other's presence would somehow violate security.

Below the tower, only the leaves on a row of quaking aspen moved. The sweet forest air cleared their lungs of the road dust. A great morning stillness enveloped the lake. It looked as if nothing had changed here for aeons until the arrival of the white man with his metal weapons and tools of destruction, yet this northwestern corner of the continent still seemed pretty much undisturbed by progress.

Chorley looked at his watch; he held up five fingers to Linkum. Five minutes to go. The other intelligence chiefs simultaneously checked their watches. Chorley looked skyward; a flight of hawks wheeled and skimmed the lake. And then it was time.

The first inkling of what was happening was the heat. They felt it as a breath of hot air, as if a Mediterranean south wind had lost its way and had been caught in a western air current; it reached a hundred feet up to the observation post and reddened their cheeks and eyes. Looking downward, they saw a cloud of steam encircling the waters, hissing and boiling. Through the misted, bubbling waters they could see flashing, leaping sunfish and pickerel struggling for air, and then the steelhead trout and salmon from the depths of the lake dancing wildly in death throes on the surface. "Dammit!" Linkum shouted, watching the dying fish. Thousands of trout lay belly up, whitened by the steaming lake. Swarms of insects and bees rose from the overhanging branches along the edges and speckled the water, suddenly fried before they could escape the rising steam. A beat of wings emptied the trees of nesting birds, and the hawks in their aeries along the tree line rose higher and higher, flying in confused circles. The ashen waters of the lake began to lower visibly, a foot every few seconds, before their eyes. The earth holding the shrubs loosened and turned into brown mud, and the rocks tumbled into the molten earth's rootholds. Now the fir trees that had stood so nobly along the narrow roadway came crashing down, broken matchsticks twisting lower and lower into the sinking water.

There came an explosive sound, like the noise of some huge cork popping out of a gigantic bottle, and a final sworl of water was sucked beneath the earth. In less than twenty minutes, the sparkling lake had become a burial-mound for everything that swam, crawled or flew. Nothing remained but a mudhole in the ground, a void of death in the forest.

From across the moribund lake a flare was sent up that hovered for a few seconds and then fizzled out in a flash of purple flame—a man-made signal that the experiment was over. The intelligence officers and their aides descended from their perch. At the foot of the observation post they were greeted by a general wearing the Chemical Warfare insigne; he was accompanied by two colonels and three civilians. He introduced them; the civilians were simply called "professors," but the general did not say where they were from nor mention their university affiliations.

"Fantastic!" declared the Chemical Warfare general. "It worked like a charm. And clean as a whistle— no radiation, no blast, not a problem, just a neat hole a hundred and seventy-five feet down the center. We pulled it off! It was tried out on some backyard ponds in Virginia, but this was the first genuine test of how to make a real body of water disappear from the face of the earth. Gurgle, gurgle everywhere and not a drop to drink."

Chorley said, "Now I understand why you changed the name of this show to Operation Stopper."

The Chemical Warfare general smiled. "It is rather a good descrition, isn't it? I named it myself. We started out calling it Operation Bathplug, but Stopper has more of a double-meaning. We can pull the plug on any lake in the world—meaning that we can dry up a country and change its whole balance of nature. Do you see the possibilities? You know, you can live without fire and freeze your nuts off but you can't last very long without water. Not even if you're a Russian peasant on the steppes. Stopper can stop the enemy when and wherever necessary. In practice, it can be used at an operative distance of—"

Hap Chorley broke in. "I don't think it's necessary to go into details, general." His tone of voice was calm and measured, but Linkum felt the ice in his words. "We're impressed."

The Army and Navy intelligence chiefs nodded.

"I'm sure that if we require more particulars from Chem Warfare we can get it later at the Pentagon. In the meantime we'll take the responsibility of reporting the results of Stopper through the Joint Chiefs to the President in his capacity as Commander-in-Chief. But no else is to hear of it—except as we determine. Understood?" Chem Warfare said it was.

A combat chopper was waiting at the far end of the runway when the Air Force medium bomber landed at Andrews after the cross-country flight. This time it was an upholstered Huey without the waist guns, big enough to carry a platoon in a search-and-destroy mission, or one very important Pentagon person and his brevetted aide.

They descended the lowered steps and, it seemed to Linkum, in less than ten minutes the Huey from Hap Chorley's private air fleet hovered over his Maryland farm. A remote-control signal from the aircraft lit up the farm's landing-pad. The chopper took off for its home base the moment they debarked.

"One bourbon and branch water before hitting the sack," Chorley said, yawning, now back in the house. He filled the glass tumblers, and they sipped their drinks slowly.

"Well, how did you like the little show? Was I fooling?"

"It made me sick to my stomach. The sight of all that grilled death, the busted-open fish and—"

"But no people, remember that. Theirs was different in Anatolia, and it'll be different again when they target a point here."

197

"And what if we take out one of their lakes?"

"The people effect will be secondary, at least. Now, let's sleep on it."

In his office at the Pentagon the next morning, Chorley busily examined the overnight messages from his men on station around the world. Linkum knew what he was looking for: reports of the Washington experiment that might have been picked up by the other side. He could not tell from the expression on Chorley's face as he studied the overnights. Time enough to know if it was part of his assignment; and he had reached the stage where he felt better knowing less.

"This is the one I've been waiting for," Chorley said. "A small thing—but now we can move on it."

"You sound mysterious."

"Not at all—the Bulgarian hard-on has received his instructions again. The show of Western European and American paintings at the Hermitage has been extended. That's for our benefit, or, rather, yours. They really want you there. You'll have to go through the routine with him again to get the invitation formally—we wouldn't want them to know that we've monitored their messages to their embassies here. Have you got that Antonello postcard?"

Linkum reached into his breast pocket and held it up.

"I carry the Madonna with me at all times," he said.

"That's what I thought," Chorley said. "You're a man on the side of the angels."

"No, the Madonnas. They're for real—the artist's

198

vision of beauty in his own time. Those cute little angels were strictly created in the artist's imagination."

"Thanks for the lecture. Now, you know what he looks like. Same meeting-place: the park bench where Sixteenth joins Florida. He'll be carrying one or more of his nudie magazines, if he's misplaced his postcard. Act surprised."

"Is there anything that I'm supposed to give him?"

"Not this time." Chorley checked his watch. "Take a cab and walk the last few blocks. He doesn't have to know where you're coming from."

Linkum followed the instructions, and got out across the street from Meridian Hill Park. This time the Bulgarian was waiting for him, casually reading a copy of *Screw.* He had refined his tastes. The Bulgarian did not wait for him to flash his postcard; instead he greeted Linkum with a grin of recognition and handed him an envelope. "Ho-kay?" He was pointing to a bare-bottomed color photograph of a young lady's pubic hair in *Hustler,* which had been chastely folded inside *Screw.* Linkum replied with a comradely locker-room leer, "Ho-kay," then pulled out the postcard of the blue-shawled Sicilian Madonna.

The Bulgarian diplomat snapped shut his magazine, lowered his head, and crossed himself solemnly.

Linkum waited until he was back in Room 3224-AF at the Pentagon before opening the message in front of Chorley.

"Same hotel?" Chorley asked, relighting his cigar.

"The Evropeiskaya."

199

"On Brodsky Street. Not bad. The hotel restaurant is one of the best in Leningrad. Try the blini, with the black and red caviar on the side. Any mention of going to Moscow first?"

"Here, why don't you read it yourself?"

Chorley took the envelope, read it quickly, running his fingers over the surface, then studied the message.

"You may be able to transact all our business right in Leningrad. Depends whether Madame Zaremba wants you to pay her a call in person at Number Two Dzerzhinsky Square in Moscow. If she does, accept the invitation. She'll be sizing you up for your manhood. You might find it educational to see what KGB head-quarters looks like, at least in the public area, where you'd think you were in a nice insurance office at coffee-break time. I've only met her once, at an official function on July Fourth, but I tell you again, she's got more guts than your lady VP at the network, what's-her-name, Delafield, take my word for it."

"I'd just as soon spend my time and your money at the Hermitage."

"Naturally, that's why you're going there, isn't it? To look at the paintings and write about the exhibition? Well, give my best to Capitano Glazunov. From the fat one who smokes the smelly cigars. And, incidentally, here's something else to give him—personally."

"A piece of paper, finally. Am I supposed to know what it says?"

"Nothing more or less than a description of what we've both seen out West. It's carefully worded and cleared for the eyes of the intelligence chiefs and our next-aboves only, which is why the paper is sealed and official-looking. They'll appreciate that—part of the game between our respective intelligence services, honor among thieves, so to speak. It makes it more appealing when you pass it along as my personal courier to say, quite honestly, that you have not read the contents yourself."

"Hugger-mugger and three Hail Marys—is this intelligence or some new religion?"

"A little of each, chum. We know how to speak each other's language. If you're questioned by them, tell them what you witnessed with your own eyes. But don't mention Stopper. The name of the operation isn't for their ears or eyes. I don't want them to put two-and-two-and-X together in case there's been any breach of security over in Chemical Warfare or by one of the publicity hounds in the President's national security entourage—including the esteemed advisor himself. I don't have to mention names. Getting your picture in the paper, the news columns or the gossip columns, is a contagious disease. Once anyone's been bitten by the bug he loses his immunity—his sense of security. You knew your sources—I call them leaks—around Washington. Vanity causes more breakdown in security than ideology. End of my lecture."

Linkum examined the sealed envelope; it really was closed by a wax seal stamped with the Air Force insigne.

"What do you mean when you say I can tell them what I saw with my own eyes?"

"Exactly that. Your reaction can mean just as much

as a straight report. You were frightened. So was I, thinking of the consequences."

"What if I'm asked how it works?"

"Well, you're not carrying any nuggets of plutonium in your knapsack or any blueprints or anything like that. The letter, by the way, more clearly indicates what you've already been told by Andrei—that they've got a seismic weapon and that we've taken their successful experiment seriously. You don't say, and we don't say, that we know they pulled it off in Turkey. That's where they know they've got us by the well-knowns. We can't accuse them without lousing up our relations with the Turkish ally and stand the chance of losing our bases and other listening-posts. I couldn't tell you how it works myself. We have to stress that we've got our own, that we'll use it unhesitatingly against them in their ballpark, and that if they try theirs again, anywhere, repeat anywhere, in the world where American lives will be lost, we'll pull the plug on one or more of their major bodies of water."

Linkum said, "Am I supposed to get something in return?"

Chorley said, "You might. Either way, it's a message. I wouldn't put much stock in a piece of paper from them at this point. No one would take the chance to commit himself, or herself, in writing there now. More than likely the reply will come in a conversation that's tapped. That will be their record, and it can also be erased if necessary. The warning from us is what counts now—as a preventive to keep them from getting too cocky after their success in Anatolia. I've convinced the

Joint Chiefs and the President himself to try this indirect route."

"The President is aware of what you're up to?"

"Of course. He had to be informed. Even your name came out as the bearer of the message. He told me that he'd been reading your stuff in the paper for years."

"I hope he hasn't read my security file and some of the things I've written about government policies. Anyway, we both know about messengers. As Sophocles or one of those wise men put it long ago, kill the messenger who bears the bad news."

"You're not the target," Chorley said. "They think less of journalists in Russia than we do. You're safer there than here. They're after bigger fish."

"That's a consolation."

"Look, we know a direct approach can't be made openly for political reasons. Publicly, some of us in the Pentagon had to make the proper hawk noises, show our talons, and keep up the hardline horseshit as if we didn't know what a nuclear exchange meant. Part of it has to do with pleasing the networks and top columnists. You come across looking good on the evening news and you can add a star or get an offer after early retirement from a multi-national."

"I've heard tell of that—"

"But on the professional level it's got to be different, especially in intelligence. You're the one who always uses the word 'pro' about your work. Well, I'm for the pros in my line too."

Linkum nodded. "The whole thing sounds like putting two scorpions in a bottle and letting them have at each other."

"May the best scorpion win," said Chorley, punching Linkum playfully. "While you're there, pick me up a couple of boxes of Havanas, old cock."

Seven

CROSSING THE Anichkov Bridge over the River Neva, the American journalist asked the Soviet museum curator if it would be possible to stop the limousine for a moment. The iron grillwork on the railing had caught his eye and he wanted to see it close-up; to touch the tridents of Neptune and prancing sea horses and abstract floral designs carved in intricate yet primitive patterns on the walkway of the graceful bridge in the center of Leningrad.

"No wonder you admire it," Glazunov said. "The bridge was designed by one of the Italian architects that were brought here by Peter and Catherine."

"It could be over the River Arno dividing Florence or Pisa instead of the Neva," Sam said. "But the design still has the solid look that I think of as Russian."

"You're talking like a Westerner nostalgic for dear old St. Petersburg. Moscow is Eastern, Leningrad is

Western, at first glance. You'll see the difference for yourself."

"Is Moscow on my official itinerary?"

"Official? Well, that depends. You're here to see the Hermitage exhibition, you know."

"What does it depend on?"

Glazunov did not answer.

The Moskva was driven by a chauffeur with big ears. Ever since picking him up, Glazunov had seemed a little nervous. In the limousine, he had talked in enigmatic circles. Brazenly, the chauffeur wore a shoulder holster that showed each time he stretched and yawned. Linkum recognized the butt of a Tula-Tokarev 7.62 mm. automatic poking up. It was not unfamiliar; Capitano Glazunov had carried one himself during their war.

The curator asked the chauffeur if it would be possible to stop the Moskva near the bridge. The chauffeur pulled into a prohibited parking zone directly on the Kutuzova Embankment. A pair of policemen, strolling by, peered at the official license plate and saluted the limousine.

Linkum and Glazunov walked the length of the Anichkov Bridge, crossed over and stopped to examine the balustrade, decorated with mythological figures pockmarked and weathered sea-green by time and the river. On the four corners of the bridgehead great bronze horses stood pawing the air, and the curator explained that they had been buried in the garden of the Palace of Pioneers for almost three years while the city was besieged by German artillery.

"Sam, you will excuse my rudeness," Glazunov said.

With a half-turn of his head, he motioned toward the chauffeur.

"That one is not a regular driver from the Hermitage. His ugly hearse of a car was assigned to me. I wanted to pick you up at the airport in my own little Moskvich, but they wanted it this way. The chauffeur is working for *them*."

"That's pretty obvious, Andrei. Don't worry about it."

"I trust I won't sound as stupid when we get our chance to be alone later." . . .

The day earlier Linkum had asked Chorley about going to Leningrad via New York so that he could see Jennie Ives. No, Chorley had told him, because time was literally of the essence now. But he had no objections if Linkum wanted to call her and say where he was going. "It's perfectly reasonable to tell her that you've got an assignment from an art magazine to cover the Hermitage exhibition—and then, of course, you can call your editor friend and tell him that you're going to be over there anyway and you'll be writing something for him." Chorley sounded pleased with himself. "Who knows, chum, you may be building a new career for yourself away from the paper. Turn your avocation into a living, unless you like my line of work so much that you'd want to stay on with me." Linkum said he didn't think so.

He placed the call from a public telephone booth near the Government Printing Office stand in the basement of the Pentagon. Jennie asked him where he was and he said, simply, Washington, getting some background material and a possible assignment from the

Smithsonian magazine, that he had a chance to do a piece on speculation, expenses paid in advance, in Leningrad. "At least you called me this time," she said. "Can you take along your best friend?" Linkum began to say he would love to, but she let him off the hook with, "Well, thanks for asking, darling, especially since I've never been to Russia either, but I'm afraid I've got too many lunch dates to break this week . . . just be sure you don't invite anyone to go in my place."

She sounded cheerful. Things at the paper, at least in the Sunday news-analysis section, were pretty much unchanged, though the Lifestyles section had become a disaster area, a mausoleum where all the upward-mobile strivers and advertisers were reincarnated as people in the trendy news. He told her that he'd be back in a week and, only half meaning it, she told him to stay on a few more days as long as someone else was paying for it.

"And be sure to call collect if you find out that the cold war is over," Jennie said, and he promised he would, if not before, and then, as they had done in a thousand phone calls, they lowered their voices and said, "I love you."

When he took the escalator up to the second ring and walked around to the Arlington side, Linkum met Chorley coming out of the two-stars-and-above men's room.

"Get cracking—you're all set on the Aeroflot flight leaving Dulles at 1730 hours. You should be in Moscow a few minutes after noon tomorrow—it's a direct flight on Sundays and Tuesdays only, and Maryjane was able to use her charms to get you a seat today."

208

Chorley handed him a thousand rubles in small denominations. "A little pocket money for tipping, which of course is not permitted in the Soviet Union, but you'll find it greases the way around the hotel and restaurants. It'll also save you time at the exchange booths. You can pay for the flight from Moscow to Leningrad—it's only eighteen rubles, or it was last week."

"No layover in Moscow?"

"Not unless Andrei fixed it. He's your contact, and we're keeping our people out of sight on this mission. You'll be on you own."

"In for a penny, in for a ruble," Linkum said. "I only have one question: Do they applaud the Russian pilots if they make a safe landing?"

"No, they give them a medal."

The high-tailed Ilyushin-62M had lifted off smoothly; below, the landmarks and roadways around the District of Columbia looked uncrowded, but the Sunday drivers were bumper-to-bumper on the Capital Beltway, going home in the late afternoon. The jetliner gained altitude, heading north. It was almost dark when the plane touched down at Gander, refueled and then sped on through the star-strewn night.

Linkum dutifully stuck to the mineral water instead of the vodka, tried out his half-dozen words of tourist Russian and avoided the slang expressions that Andrei had taught him in the months they had shared the same quarters in Italy, not knowing if they were acceptable in polite chitchat with the buxom Aeroflot hostesses. Most of the passengers seemed to be businessmen, including two stolid groups from Japan and East Germany, and he

209

watched to see if anyone from the airline paid particular attention to him. None, that he noticed, did. He pulled out a worn Modern Library edition of *Best Russian Short Stories* that he had bought at a wartime stopover in Gander, long ago when the United States and the Soviet Union were allied and he felt a need to catch up on their literature, and he fell asleep rereading Ivan Bunin's "The Gentleman from San Francisco."

Just before noon the Ilyushin began its descent, and Linkum could peer over the landscape of towns and cultivated soil and sparkling lakes. The plane landed, to no applause, faultlessly. As he walked down the ramp, a young woman from Intourist stepped up and exclaimed, "Welcome to Moscow!" He was about to ask her how she had spotted him among the passengers when she said, "You look better, younger, than your photograph, Mr. Linkum." He wondered which one it was: an old visa picture, something exchanged through the East Berliners when he had gone inside the Checkpoint Charlie maze, or a hidden camera when he had met the Bulgarian in the Washington park. Well, if his mug shot was in the Pentagon files without his knowledge, it might as well be at No. Two Dzerzhinsky Square; an unemployed newspaperman needed all the recognition he could get.

He breezed through Sheremetievo Airport's tight visa control when the Intourist guide whispered a few magic words. On the other side of the desk for those holding diplomatic passports, his luggage was waiting. He was not asked to open the combination lock or to show his ordinary passport. Instead of leaving the airport for Moscow he was handed a ticket by the Intourist guide. "I hope you will have a very pleasant journey to your next destination—Leningrad," she said sweetly. "It is one of the U.S.S.R.'s most historical cities, founded in 1924, modern era."

That took care of Moscow. She glanced at her watch. "The connecting flight leaves in just twelve minutes. I shall be happy to take you to the proper gate." She accompanied him on the bus out to the flight line, said something to the steward that caused a stare toward Linkum, and waved him aboard the Tupolev-154A shuttle to Leningrad.

In little more than an hour, he was greeting Andrei, then pulled out a phrase book and said, *"Ya gavaryoo' to'lka pa anglee'skee,* Capitano Andrei,"

Glazunov roared with laughter. "What do you mean you speak only English? That is the first Russian I have ever heard spoken with a Sicilian accent! You speak like a true Southerner from Moscow, Capitano Sam."

"But I never got there, Andrei."

"Moscow is Washington, Leningrad is New York—artistically." He shrugged. "You're better off here if your time is limited."

"Is it, Andrei?"

"That depends."

Again without going through formalities, they passed the security barriers at Pulkovo Airport, entered the waiting limousine, and were driven along Primorsky Prospekt into the city. . . .

Returning now to the car after walking across the Anichkov Bridge, Glazunov ordered the driver to go directly to the Evropeiskaya Hotel. Linkum kept swiveling his head and asking about the magnificent buildings and squares and bridges; everywhere there were stone lions and sphinxes and a bestiary of real and imaginary creatures adorning the czarist facades, well-preserved from or restored after the wartime bombings. They passed through a square of palaces and small theatres before turning into Nevsky Prospekt—Andrei called it "the main drag" of Leningrad—and Brodsky Street. The Evropeiskaya, on the outside, appeared as classical as its neighboring buildings, but when Linkum entered the lobby he found it decorated in art nouveau style.

"I think the same Italian artisans put the rosettes on the walls and ceilings that did the job in my room in the Grande Albergo e delle Palme in Palermo," Linkum said, and Glazunov agreed. "If not the same ones, their cousins or uncles. Is the room okay?" Linkum nodded. "This must be the bridal suite—I'm glad I took along some extra rubles," and Glazunov told him, "You're the guest of the Hermitage Museum." "In that case, I'll buy the dinner," Linkum said.

Glazunov nudged him. "After all that flying you should take a siesta. No more sightseeing for now. I will come by to pick you up, in my own car, at half-past seven for dinner. If you have not done so already, fix your watch to our time." He had forgotten to, and set it ahead eight hours.

Before dozing off, Linkum thought of Hap Chorley's doublefaced chronometer that showed the time in Washington and Moscow simultaneously—"ICBM mean time," he called it—so he would never forget where his mind was at.

And he also thought of the two uniformed security police that he had noticed standing across the street from the Evropeiskaya, almost casually dangling Kalashnikova rifles from their shoulders, muzzles down but with curved clips in.

Linkum awoke sleepily to his own travel alarm clock's insistent ring a half-hour before Glazunov was due. He carefully did a check of the suite: first, the bottom of the telephone for a concealed microphone; he assumed that the line itself was tapped. Then, the obvious: behind the gilt-framed prints of old St. Petersburg and Petrograd and even, what the hell, under the four-poster bed. Finally, the windows: he lifted them up slightly to see if any wires led down from the bedroom, if there were any remote-control amplifiers. But it was not possible to look behind the wide moulding or the plaster rosettes ten feet overhead. Maybe he had lost his touch, but he found nothing.

Unpacking his clothing, he put his suits in the closet and shirts in the bureau drawer, then placed the envelope that Hap Chorley had given him inside his suitcase and locked the combination. Taking a piece of nylon dental floss, he twisted so that he would know if an attempt was made to twirl the numbers on the lock. He had carried the envelope on his person during the Aeroflot flights, but he decided that he would learn more about who was to be trusted and where Glazunov stood by leaving it in his room. Ironically, it would be meaningless to anyone not involved in the exchange process.

The house phone lit up; Andrei was in the lobby and Sam told him to come up.

In the room, he noticed that Andrei also checked the bottom of the telephone box while making what he said was a call to one of his assistants at the museum. Linkum felt oddly reassured.

"Are we dining alone? I was hoping to meet your wife."

Glazunov shrugged. "We have an old proverb in Leningrad: Pray once when going to war, pray twice when going to sea, but pray thrice when going to get married."

"I guess that means I won't see her."

"She spends a good deal of time in the country with her sisters. She loves her sisters, her aunts, her cousins, her nephews, they have a good time together and I have a good time by myself, and with my work."

"Are you separated—or is that prying?"

"No, we're together, but we go our separate ways—which is, I suspect what keeps us married."

"They call that open marriage in the States. Is there a name for it in the Soviet Union?"

"Oh yes. Here, it is just called marriage."

Linkum nodded. "That may be a more honest way to put it."

"In any case, we have another old saying here: A good friend is better than a hundred relatives." . . .

Off the lobby Linkum admired the stained-glass panels in the dining room and suggested that they might eat there.

"The Vostochnyi restaurant is good here but it's

214

always filled with tourists," Glazunov said. "I've made a reservation for us at the Sadko right down the street on the Nevsky Prospekt. The menu is more traditional and the music is livelier when they have it."

Three balalaikas strummed in the background for a torch singer of many years imitating Edith Piaf. They dined on small spicy cakes of mutton and rice and pickled red beets and black bread and strong tea from a soda-fountain glass. Linkum said that it was his turn to pay and pulled out a fistful of rubles. Glazunov excitedly asked him if they had been exchanged at the Moscow airport and when Linkum replied that he had brought the rubles with him, Glazunov said, "You must watch the currency laws." Then he concealed the rubles under the tablecloth and said that he would pay the check with them and returned the excess money to Linkum. "A different set of policemen worry about such matters," Glazunov said. "We don't need some upstart mixing into our affairs. Sometimes a flea can bite harder than an elephant."

After dinner they strolled along the Nevsky and off into its side streets and broad squares past a rainbow of marble memorials and granite columns and castellated towers, wandering next to centuries-old monuments to imperial decadence decorated in mosaics of malachite and lapis lazuli and preserved for the bureaucrats of the new order. Glazunov pointed to a row of rooming houses that appeared to lean over one of the nameless small canals, and said that Raskolnikov had lived here, had gone from the Hay Market to the house where he killed the old woman money-lender through Dostoyevskyan alleyways like these, making the fictional character a real presence in the darkness; and Sam reminded Andrei that, once in Rome, he had shown him the crooked streets where Henry James had meandered, intoxicated by the sight of the spouting Triton in Piazza Barberini and finally seeing the Colosseum in Daisy Miller's romanticized moonlight.

"If you are tired, save a little for tomorrow," Andrei said, but Sam told him that he had gotten a second wind, stimulated by names and places that leaped out of the pages of literature and history—the Pushkin Theatre and Gorki Prospekt, Herzen Street and Decembrists Square—and what was that creamy building that looked like a combination of the Doges Palace in Venice and the Medici Palace in Florence?, and Andrei replied that it would have astonished the imported Italian architects to learn that their princely palazzo was now used as Aeroflot's city terminal. They continued on, traversing the Fontanka Canal and the winding Moika River that fed into the Neva, until Linkum had walked his feet off and confessed as much.

Heading back to the Evropeiskaya, Glazunov remarked that if you looked behind them, all of Leningrad's buildings told tales of uprisings and abortive revolts and of the Revolution itself. But the far past was the dead past. What lived in memory here was the great siege of the city in the fourth decade of the century, through white nights and freezing winters when Hitler's artillerymen and dive bombers had turned homes and lives into rubble.

"Let me show you something," Glazunov said.

216

Passing an ordinary building on the Nevsky Prospekt, they stopped in front of an old wooden sign. Glazunov lit a match and illuminated the words, then translated them:

*"Citizens! During the shelling, this side
of the street is most* DANGEROUS.*"*

Glazunov said, "It's an ugly ikon but the most important one on the Nevsky. There must be similar signs in London and some of the other blitzed cities, or there should be. Luckily, no such signs were needed in New York, Chicago, Atlanta or Los Angeles. I hope they never take this one down. It helps people here, and I hope elsewhere, to understand this war and the cold war."

In front of the Evropeiskaya, Glazunov asked Linkum if he wanted to have some fun or at least a drink. In the shadows across the street both men caught the gleam of the Kalashnikovas carried by the security police. Linkum said that all he wanted to do now was take a bath and go to sleep.

A short time later, alone in his room, Linkum examined the entwined dental floss around the combination lock of his luggage. It had been tampered with but unopened; the envelope was still inside.

The next day when Glazunov was alone in his office overlooking the Hanging Garden at the Hermitage, Sam passed him the envelope bearing the waxed Air Force seal. "This is for you from Hap Chorley. Do you have something for me?"

"No, Sam, I do not."

"I thought you might."

"Did I promise you something? If so—"

"Not that I recall. So much has happened since we met in Palermo—"

"We have a different way of doing things here. As you no doubt know."

"Two different ways. That's why I'm here."

"I, personally, would have been happy to come to see you in the States. In that case, I might have been carrying an envelope to you."

"That isn't the reason I'm going away empty-handed, is it?"

"I did not say that. All I said was that I myself cannot reciprocate. I was not extended an invitation to visit you. That would have been necessary."

"I don't have a museum, Andrei. I haven't even got a job at this moment."

"That I am sorry about. It is why we were happy to invite you to see the extended exhibition at the Hermitage."

"Is that why? Let's stop playing cat-and-mouse."

Glazunov put his fingers to his lips and moved out from behind his desk then said loudly:

"What you say is very amusing indeed. It reminds me of what Catherine the Great once wrote about the riches in this palace when she considered everything her personal possessions. She said: 'Only the mice and I can admire all this.' And that was the attitude of the czars, until the Revolution, when all the treasures were opened for all the people to enjoy."

He motioned to Linkum to follow him outside into the open air of the Hanging Garden between two galleries.

"Sam, I can talk more freely here than in my office. You understand why?"

"Of course, I should have guessed why you were speaking in official tones. Sorry if I sounded angry."

"I cannot say for sure that my office is bugged, but why take the risk? I have been away from the intelligence service too long to know what is procedure internally—"

"I understand . . . I'm an amateur myself . . . which I guess is why I didn't take enough precautions last evening when we were out to dinner."

"How do you mean that? You were with me all the time."

"Yes . . . well, someone went through my things. Pretty clumsily too, I might say. I had a book of Russian short stories sitting on the table next to my bed. It was examined—I know, because my place mark was moved. It must have fallen out, and whoever stuck it back put it in the wrong page."

"That doesn't sound too serious. Was it a book of writings by dissidents, refuseniks? That would have been a little indiscreet to bring in, at least in the eye of the censors, who worry themselves about such things."

"No, the authors were all safely dead in this collection. Pushkin and Gogol, Kuprin and Bunin, some of the obvious ones. I don't see—"

"The literary policemen wear different glasses, Sam. Kuprin wrote about pogroms and prostitutes and other such unpleasant subjects, and Bunin preferred to live in Italy or France instead of Stalin's Russia. But that would be beyond the knowledge of the ordinary intelligence agent with light fingers. Did you find anything else disturbed in your room?"

For an instant Linkum thought to tell him, then replied, "Not that I noticed."

Glazunov now held the envelope in his hand; that was, after all, why he had come all this way. He had also wanted to see if he could find out how close Glazunov stood to the KGB. Well, the fact that they were talking outside his office bugs said something about Glazunov's own distrust and his standing with the intelligence higher-ups.

So he thought.

Glazunov held the sealed envelope in his hand, examined it carefully. "I don't think I will open it."

"But it's for you."

"No, it does not have my name on it, as you know. It would be safer for me to have someone else take care of it from this point on. Do you know what it says?"

Before Sam could answer, Glazunov looked around nervously and nodded to two members of the curatorial staff strolling by along the walkway. They stopped and leaned against the stone cherubim in the Hanging Garden, standing within earshot.

"Well, my friend," Glazunov said loudly, for their benefit, "I hope you write a good article about our wing and the exhibit. It has been extended by popular demand."

Glazunov returned to his office and pocketed the sealed envelope, then rang for his assistant, a beautiful woman in her early thirties, hidden behind horn-rimmed spectacles.

"Oriana, Mr. Sam Linkum and I are going to look at the exhibition. He is the famous American art critic —yes, the same one I have spoken about. We were in the war together. This is Oriana Lhevinne, the prettiest art curator in the Hermitage."

The flaxen-haired Oriana blushed and said, with what sounded like an English accent, "I am most pleased to make your acquaintance. I trust you will enjoy our show."

"She studied as an exchange scholar at the Tate in London," Glazunov said. "She is an expert on Turner and Moore."

"I regret we are weak in both, Mr. Linkum. But perhaps some day we will have them represented here."

The two men walked on parquet floors under the sparkling chandeliers to a grand marble staircase that led to the second tier, where palatial rooms housed the collections, country by country, of the Department of Western European Art.

"We can talk more quietly here, without interruptions. No problems with Oriana—she's not one of *them*. In fact, she is one of my dear companions. But I do not want to get her involved in this aspect of our mutual interests, you understand? She has a brother who emigrated to Israel, so she is under suspicion herself. Now, Sam, what does the message contain?"

"I haven't read it myself."

Glazunov reached into his jacket and pulled out a postcard: Antonello da Messina's shawled Madonna.

"All right, here's my copy. Produce yours so you will be able to speak to me. I am Glazunov, you are Linkum, remember?"

"No, seriously, Andrei, I am not reluctant to tell you what I know but I can't tell you what I don't know."

They entered Room 336. It was labeled, "Art of the United States of America—Twentieth Century."

"So at the right moment you will tell me what you *do* know, correct? Now, let me show you a few of the works. Most of the paintings here are by the famous American artist Rockwell Kent. The Hermitage owns twenty-six Kents."

Linkum smiled. "He's considered old-fashioned now."

"We could use a little more of your degenerate art," Glazunov said. "Do you think the walls of the Hermitage would come tumbling down if a Jackson Pollock hung right in the center of this room?"

"No—just your head."

They sat down on an ornately carved bench in a corner of the American room. No one else was around. Glazunov tapped his jacket pocket that held the sealed envelope and said, "Thank you for carrying this for me. I know that you are taking time out of your life. But let us continue what we began to discuss in the amphitheatre at Segesta. The stakes are very high—the highest.

But the game of survival is worth the chance. Even if one of us gets hurt."

"What do you mean by that, Andrei?"

Glazunov shrugged.

"I have already received my instructions. I am going to hand over the envelope, unopened, to my KGB contact in Leningrad. Like myself, he is an old reservist, but he attained the rank of colonel. It will be in the hands of Madame Zaremba in Moscow tonight. Now, is there something that I should know—for my own sake?"

Linkum wondered if this was the time and place to talk; to follow his own instructions from Chorley. And he thought: If I can't trust Andrei, if he represents nothing, neither do I.

"Andrei, the memorandum inside that envelope contains explosive facts. Hap Chorley said that I could underscore its contents and importance. I believe it points out two things: first, the American military knows that the Soviet military has a devastating seismic weapon—and that it has been tested successfully. And, second, that the American military has its own thermal weapon—and it too has been tested successfully."

"Thermal? The sun?"

"It's not something that's theoretical, Andrei. It's real. I saw it work."

"How? Through the barrel of a gun? In a fire-bomb?"

"I don't know the precise formula and they wouldn't tell me and I probably wouldn't want to know, anyway. But this much I do know because I saw it with my own eyes: a large body of water existed in its natural

223

state and then, in less than one hour, it was gone. Kaput. Wiped off the face of the earth. Nothing left but a huge hole in the ground."

Glazunov said, "So now the score is even again. Two inmates with dangerous weapons at loose from the same asylum."

"Or two scorpions in a bottle?"

"I hope not," Glazunov said. "But it makes more sense for both to know what they have. Now, for the first time, I can understand the plan a little more clearly. It is safer with two countries to have an atom bomb than one. And it is better for the U.S.A. and the U.S.S.R. to know about the so-called next generation of weapons each country has. At best that way leads to a stalemate. At worst, to madness."

"Well, now you know as much as I do, Andrei."

But in so saying, Sam also knew that he had deliberately omitted one salient fact: the warning. That could, should, wait for the time when he elaborated on Operation Stopper to the KGB itself. After all, someone had tampered with his briefcase.

Glazunov said, "I have some work to do. Once I deliver this missive to the colonel, my task will be over. Yours, too, I hope. Let them handle it on the highest intelligence levels."

Linkum nodded. "I'll wander around the exhibition and some of the Western European rooms. This should be a feast for the *distinguished* American art critic."

"I'll send Oriana around in case you get lost—but not a word of our other business to her."

"Of course not. She doesn't have to escort me, but it would be pleasant. I'll probably be—"

"She'll know where you are going the moment I leave you—to the Italian and French rooms."

"How did you guess?"

Glazunov laughed. "No Antonellos, but everybody else—including the Picassos at the turning-point of his career."

Linkum nodded and descended the grand staircase to the first floor, looking out on the Palace Embankment, then oriented himself with a pocket guide. He headed for Room 214 to see the two Leonardos in the Hermitage. As he stared at one titled *Madonna with a Flower*, he found Oriana standing at his side.

"I see you found what you were looking for," she said.

"And you found me rather quickly."

"I assumed that you would come here."

"So did Andrei. I hope I'm not intruding on your time—"

"Unless you want to be alone with the paintings, it is an honor. And it gives me an opportunity to use my English."

"Don't listen to my accent too closely or it might ruin yours."

Oriana smiled sweetly; and, standing next to her and smelling her hair, Linkum thought of Jennie.

"That Leonardo is not the best one here," Oriana said. "Somebody restored it a little too zealously a few centuries ago. The poor Madonna has no eyebrows and the Child looks stuffed with macaroni."

225

Linkum smiled. "I've never heard it put so well. Do you have anything in the Hermitage by Guardi?"

"We have the same tastes. Yes, we've got three Guardis in Room 236, a landscape, a seascape and a townscape, all with lots of little figures in them."

"All talking with their hands and bodies, and nobody seems to be listening."

"That's Guardi, all right," she said. "Now it is my turn to say well put."

"By the way, where is the special exhibit of American and Western European Art?"

Oriana looked puzzled. "That ended a week ago. It was nothing special—just two rooms with a retrospective of some of the works from the collection as a whole. They are now back in their original places."

Linkum nodded. "I was just curious because I'd been under the impression that the exhibit was extended."

They walked into the rooms containing no less than thirty-six Picassos. "Only a few of these have traveled," she said, "and not the major ones." They stood in front of the pioneering *Dance of the Veils*, which had helped to define Cubism as much as any painting. "Originally from the Leo and Gertrude Stein collection, then bought by one of the private Russian collectors before the Revolution, and now here at the Hermitage," she explained, then hesitantly said, "an interesting woman, Gertrude Stein, from all that I have read. A great patron, and a writer herself. I am of the same religious faith."

She glanced at him quickly for a reaction.

"Yes, Andrei mentioned that you have relatives living in Israel. Have you ever been there?"

She shook her head.

"A civilized country in a desert world. It's really astonishing to see. I covered a few of its wars. The museum in Jerusalem has a sculpture garden that blends into those ancient hills. At sunset, the sculpture has a golden glow."

"I would like to see that some time. If I am allowed to go there," Oriana said, as though to herself.

Linkum found himself devoutly hoping that she would make it some day, but he refrained from predicting that she would.

As the closing bell for vistors clanged they walked back to the curatorial offices, and he found himself wondering about the meaning of the nonexistent American exhibition. Either Andrei had expected him to arrive in Leningrad soon after the first invitation had been issued or he had not expected him to show up at all. The exhibition seemed like a pretext. Linkum wondered if his failure to appear immediately had caused any problems for Andrei with those he reported to—in Leningrad or Moscow.

He decided not to question Glazunov about the special exhibit, not in front of Oriana. The covert assignment both were carrying out was off the ground; the Hermitage show was only a cover story. And the paintings, the masterpieces, were still in place for him, and not just for Catherine and the palace mice. He wished that he did have a week to wander around the Hermitage

227

and the more human museum outside the walls, Leningrad itself, but he would settle for a few days here.

"I trust that Oriana did not fill your head with too much propaganda," Glazunov said.

So he had returned from seeing his colonel.

"Absolutely," Linkum said. "She made the most subversive remarks I have ever heard about the Renaissance painters—and the wisest."

Oriana blushed; another one of her appealing qualities, he thought. Blushing was a rare reflecting mirror of modesty in immodest times.

Linkum said that he hoped they could both join him for dinner, and Andrei, looking at her, said they would pick him up at about half-past eight. He declined a lift in the Moskvich and walked back alone along the Nevsky Prospekt.

When he picked up his key at the Evropeiskaya, the concierge handed him two messages: The first was from Glazunov: Please call me immediately at my office at the Hermitage, tel. 12-57-43. The second was a cablegram: RUSH SAMPLE MUSEUM POSTCARDS. It was signed: Guardi Art Company, Baltimore, Maryland.

Linkum knew what the second message meant. It required no answer; he knew it meant the red ball was up.

He rang Glazunov's number.

"Sam? What took you so long to get back to the hotel?" Excitement elevated his voice for the first time. "Well, it must have been a very leisurely walk, but I have been trying to reach you for at least one hour. Stay there. I will be right over to explain why."

228

In less than ten minutes he was knocking on the door. He looked around the room, then motioned Linkum to follow him into the bathroom—away from the ceiling bugs.

"I'm sorry, my friend, but we cannot have dinner tonight. That KGB limousine is downstairs waiting. My instructions are that you are to leave immediately for Moscow. A plane is standing by to fly you there."

"Are you joining me?"

"I asked the same question. They said no. That is why I wanted to see you before you were summoned downstairs. I wanted to say goodbye."

"What do you suppose the rush is all about?"

"The information in the envelope. Are you sure there is not more in it that I should know?"

"I told you all I knew, Andrei."

"Of course. Well, dear friend, we have come this far together. It has been a long journey. I am happy that we met here. "

"I only scratched the surface of the Hermitage and the city."

"Good. That means you will return in a calmer time, I hope."

"Will you tell Oriana how much I regret not being able to dine with both of you tonight?"

"Of course."

"And that I hope, some day soon, she will be free to go where she wants?"

"Understood, yes."

Glazunov extended his hand; and they embraced.

"Well, I hope we accomplish what we set out to do.

In Leningrad, we have an old saying: Convictions are not like gloves—one cannot change them easily. I believe you and I are both men with similar convictions, Sam."

"Capitano."

Dusk descended over the palaces and canals and domes of Leningrad and then clouds glided past the moon, darkening Pulkovo Airport. The black limousine pulled up in front of a modified Mig-21 parked at the southern end of a runway reserved for military aircraft in camouflaged revetments. Instead of using the combat rollback canopy, steps were lowered from an emergency exit and Linkum was directed to clamber into one of the two upholstered seats behind the pilot.

No one else was aboard. There would have been a place for Andrei if they'd wanted him. A coil of wires snaked down from the pilot's helmet. Linkum was glad to see that no oxygen tube was attached, which meant they would fly at a normal altitude and he would not have to be hooked up to breathe. He did not want to be sucking air. Once, as an observer on a Fortress mission against the marshalling yards at Frankfurt am Main, Luftwaffe interceptors had knocked out the electrical system and he had found himself lightheaded until they were over friendly territory. For this mission he especially wanted to keep his wits and his mind clear.

The KGB was apparently in one very great hurry to see him, otherwise why would he be summoned to Moscow so soon, minutes probably, after the Air Force envelope came into their hands? At most, the Mig would save only a half-hour over the commercial Tupolev shuttle flight. He wondered if anything special was in the wind; if there could be more in the message than he had learned from Hap Chorley in almost-casual conversation. Whatever the message contained, it was clear that the KGB did not want the second team in Leningrad to handle him.

The Russian fighter plane spun in short bursts onto a side runway and climbed almost vertically into the sky. Peering out the window and straining over his shoulder, he saw the orange flame of the afterburner licking the darkness. The Mig reminded him of Chorley's fancy medium bomber; so Zaremba had her little air fleet too.

Chorley. The Guardi Art Company. The cablegram from "Baltimore" at the Evropeiskaya. The prearranged signal had been half-joke. "You'll be incommunicado while over with the Russkies," Hap had said. "I can't phone you from here or the farm—and you're not to try to get in touch with me. Unless some dire emergency comes up such as a tummyache or self-inflicted wound while shaving, in which case you can call the consulate in Leningrad or the embassy in Moscow and ask for a doctor, just like any other tourist." And then Chorley had turned serious. "There's a remote possibility that I may want you back here very quickly for one reason or another. If I do, you fly the first commercial out of Moscow and then change for an American carrier in London or Paris for the flight to Washington." Linkum had said he understood that something might come up, but he could not imagine what because the mission of passing an envelope struck him as a milk run. "We'll need a code," Hap had said, not directly responding. "Got any ideas?" And he had suggested using his old Guardi mail drop. Hap then said, "If I signal you to rush back the postcards, that means haul ass fast and head home for Washington."

But he did not dare to acknowledge the cable or to show any panic. He had no choice; General Zaremba was at the end of the line—the only one who could make things happen. He had to play out his hand. This was *his* decision, and it felt good, he had to admit, finally to be doing something besides taking Hap's orders.

Abruptly he felt a hard tug on his safety harness. The nose of the Mig pointed sharply downward. He glanced at his watch: they had been airborne only twenty-two minutes. As they began their approach, he spotted yellow runway lights but no other landmarks. The engines of the fighter screamed in reverse as soon as the tricycle landing-gear touched down. The pilot did a one-eighty and they taxied to a hangar. Its doors opened and as quickly closed behind the Mig. Standing by was a twin of the black Moskva that had picked him up in Leningrad. The chauffeur saluted, helped him with his bag, said nothing. Only the pilot, stepping down from the pulled-back canopy, looked directly at him for the first time and broke into a wide grin, as if to say, No flies on me.

This much was clear: it was not Sheremetievo International Airport. The limousine circled a barbed-wire chain fence and then, leaving the military aerodrome somewhere outside Moscow, quickly picked up speed on a broad highway. By his calculations they drove in silence for eighteen minutes—he knew that Chorley would ask him for precise times to determine his location and the direction taken to Dzerzhinsky Square. But they were not heading for the center of Moscow; rather, somewhere on the outskirts, with trees and glades. He caught sight of and tried to memorize a sign: Pervaya Ostankinskaya.

The Moskva drew up beneath a porte-cochere, and the chauffeur hurried around to open the passenger door for him. Entering what appeared to be a manor house on a wooded estate, decorated with gilt carvings on the portals and cornices, he followed a row of illuminated chandeliers, walking on the parquetry of what could have been a ballroom, past fireplaces faced with tiles of marble malachite. All around the walls were oil paintings with themes in marked contrast to the eighteenth-century wooden panels and scrolls: heroic figures standing tall and armed with long bayonets and muscular, larger-than-life peasants and workers listening attentively to lectures delivered by leaders in fields and factories. At the far end of the great room four men and a woman were seated at long circular divans. As he approached them, the woman rose and walked toward him slowly with the help of a cane.

"Welcome, Captain Linkum."

"Mr. Linkum. I am not in the military."

"As you wish. My name is Zaremba."

"I'm pleased to meet you, general."

She was taller and somewhat more elegant than he had imagined, her hair longer and less-coiffed than the women he had observed on Leningrad's streets. She was dressed in a very good imitation of a Chanel suit. Chorley had told him that she was in her mid-fifties and that, while serving as a junior political officer with a front-line battalion in the defense of Moscow, she had been wounded by German shrapnel and walked with some difficulty. Of her personal life, USAFSS had no information.

She invited Linkum to join her on the sofa and introduced her colleagues. They were obviously of lower rank, deferring to her. It looked like a social gathering.

"We appreciate your taking the time to come to Moscow. Did you have a pleasant flight?"

"It was rather hurried. I would rather have flown in one of your commercial planes, as I did going to Leningrad. I prefer civilian aircraft."

"Oh, we thought you would enjoy a ride in a Mig —not many Americans get the chance."

"Well, it was certainly quick enough, but I would have enjoyed staying a little longer to see more of the masterworks at the Hermitage Museum."

"Well, perhaps you can return to Leningrad. Would tomorrow or the next day be convenient?"

"No, I'm afraid not."

"Oh, I am sorry to hear that, Mr. Linkum, especially since you have come all this way. Is there any special reason why you are in such a hurry to return to the United States? Would you be going to Washington or Baltimore or your home in New York?"

Linkum thought for an instant, then said, "It's only that I've said my goodbyes to my friends in Leningrad and I wouldn't want to inconvenience them again—"

"Friends? You know some others in addition to Captain Glazunov?"

He knew that he had let something slip, and she had caught him. The only other person he had met—undoubtedly had been spotted talking to in the galleries—was Oriana Lhevinne.

"No, just Andrei—as you know, we were friends during the war." He could have kicked himself for implying any friendship, even any knowledge of Oriana, who was probably under surveillance because of her religion and beliefs. Hurriedly he went on, "Very good friends in the war against Nazism and Fascism. We worked together recovering stolen art. He is respected internationally in his field—"

"Yes, we have read his papers in various foreign journals."

"So have I."

They paused. Madame Zaremba or, more accurately here, General Zaremba, had won the first round in their sparring.

She turned to one of the KGB aides from her Fifth Directorate and suggested that Mr. Linkum might wish to have something cold to drink. The youngest of the military aides—all in uniformly ash-gray suits and flowered ties—snapped his fingers and a waiter immediately arrived, bearing bottles of vodka, seltzer and something that resembled Coca-Cola in bubbling color. She tapped the vodka bottle, and the white-jacketed waiter filled her glass. Only then did the others apparently feel free to follow her tastes, and theirs.

"Vodka is best drunk ice cold," she said pleasantly.

"Yes, I've had it that way years ago with Glazunov, but this time I'd like to try that interesting-looking version of Coke, if you don't mind."

She shrugged. "Coca-colonization! You see, it really is everywhere."

They all laughed.

He sipped the overly sweet drink, and smiled in sickly approval, disliking as he did even the American original.

"I trust that you will join us in a second round of vodka," she said. The look on his face from the fake cola did not get by her.

He glanced around the room and thought that this might be the right moment to find out where they were in relation to Moscow.

"Am I very wrong in thinking that this was once used as a dance hall?"

"No doubt, but what is more relevant is that this old mansion was built by serfs, Mr. Linkum. That is why it can be truly considered as a Soviet building even though it preceded the Revolution by more than a hundred years."

He nodded. That was an original way of looking at the creation of others in the past, he thought, but he still did not know the location. He tried again.

"There are many interesting modern paintings on these walls."

"I trust you like them. We shipped the ones we found here to the Pushkin and Hermitage—they actually fought over them. The usual religious art of no special relevance today. I myself prefer paintings that tell a story, that inspire people, don't you?"

"I like all kinds and all centuries—as long as you can see the hand of genius somewhere."

She shrugged. "I hope the realism does not bother you, but of course, art is something personal, unlike mathematics, which is orderly and finite."

He remembered that Hap Chorley had told him that her field was originally mathematics.

"I admire your taste in working quarters," Linkum went on. "I'd hoped to have the opportunity to see you in Moscow itself—at Dzerzhinsky Square."

Madame Zaremba laughed. "We are everywhere, in the city as well as in the country—just like similar organizations in Washington. I hope you are not disappointed."

"Only that I won't have the chance to explore Moscow."

"You seem to know the location of our headquarters."

"But I don't know this fine building or where it is."

"Outside Moscow, Mr. Linkum."

And that ended that.

General Zaremba now turned to one of her aides and said something to him in a low voice. He reached into a leather case and handed the Air Force envelope to her. The seal, of course, was broken. She tapped the envelope on the oak table in front of the sofa.

"I am a little disappointed in this document," she said. "It is unsigned. It states little, if anything, that is not known to us."

Linkum said, cautiously, "It's authentic, that I can assure you. The United States Air Force seal should certainly make it official."

"Are you familiar with its contents?"

"More or less. And I'm authorized to state that it comes to you on the highest authority—from Henry H. Chorley, director of the Air Force Security Service."

One of the gray-suited aides broke in, "We know his duties and name." He sounded very self-satisfied.

Zaremba glared at him, and Linkum realized that they also spoke and understood English.

"You mean that you have not read this document personally?"

"No, general, I have not. So as to assure that it would be a personal communication for you, from him. It goes beyond my special assignment. I'm a courier—the same as Andrei."

"Well, I do not know precisely what you mean by courier. For rubles, for example? You brought in undeclared funds and failed to go through the proper exchange procedure at the Vneshtorgbank for foreigners. Then you passed along some of your rubles to a Soviet citizen."

Suddenly he recalled handing the dinner money to Andrei and his cautionary remarks; even something as minor as that they had been watched.

"Madame Zaremba," he said, beginning to lose his temper, "do you really believe that I came all the way to the Soviet Union to play games for a few dollars or rubles? You know that the stakes are much higher. I was a guest of the Hermitage and I volunteered, over Andrei's objections, to pay for our dinner. Now if that—"

"Mr. Linkum," she said with a wave of her hand, "I was not accusing you of anything. I was only making an observation."

He had become angry instead of remaining cool, and about nonsense at that; she had outmaneuvered him again.

Zaremba tapped her glass, and the waiter refilled hers with vodka, then removed Sam's cola drink and poured him a glass of vodka too.

"Bravo!" she declared, and her aides applauded him. They were all smiles again.

"Now, Mr. Linkum, you mentioned that you were familiar with the document. What do you mean—more or less?"

"Well, to answer any questions you may have about its points."

"In that case you must know a great deal for a simple courier. But please, no offense. Now, there is talk here of a seismic weapon. Some sort of fantastic secret weapon in the hands of the Soviet Union. We have many weapons in our arsenal, but the most important one is the strength and resolve of our leaders and people."

"General, you know the one the document refers to. It has been tested and it works."

"Where, and when? The document does not say. What are your facts?"

"I can't give you specifics on time and place of what is, after all, *your* weapon. All I can convey—and I believe it is quite important—is that American intelligence on the highest level, the National Security Agency, is, one,

239

aware of your weapon, two, knows it has been tested practically, and three, takes it very seriously."

He knew that she was probing him for his knowledge about their experiment in Turkey—especially about the effects on the American listening-posts. And he knew that he had to keep his mouth shut.

"The document also refers to your so-called thermal weapon. But every country, Mr. Linkum, including some of the fascistic ones under your control in Latin America, no doubt, has made an effort to control the environment. Again, I ask you, where and when?"

Linkum took a sip of the vodka, savoring its smooth and deceptively clear flavor.

"General, I can and will tell you more about it. I saw the weapon tested with my own eyes. I was allowed to observe the test only to be able to tell you about its effects. A certain body of water within the continental United States—it doesn't matter where—existed one day in a beautiful setting. The next day it was gone. This body of water was quite large, similar no doubt to those in Europe. In less than one hour, it disappeared—sucked under the earth. And everything around it, every living thing, was steamed to death."

Zaremba and her aides heard him out carefully. Linkum realized that they did not have to take notes; that his words were being recorded, and that every phrase, and his voice level, would be searched later for hidden meanings.

"How recent was this experiment of yours?"

Linkum hoped to find out if Zaremba already knew all about Operation Stopper through some breach in

U.S. security or some long-range detection device of their own. He realized that by answering her question he might be giving away more than he was supposed to. There must have been earth sounds; disturbances in the atmosphere, something that could be tracked by satellite photograph. Even on that remote lake in the State of Washington.

And in as blind a response as he could think of at the moment, he said, "It occurred not long ago."

It was too much to expect that, sitting here somewhere at a KGB Fifth Directorate headquarters, they would reveal what, if anything, they already knew when he could not even discover where he was "outside Moscow."

"Is there anything else you wish to tell me?"

"Yes, general, there is. I was informed by Henry H. Chorley that what I am about to say is not in the document I carried here from Washington. He did not want to make it appear belligerent, but he told me to add a warning in person as if it came directly from him, speaking for the highest level of government. It is this: If your seismic weapon is set off again anywhere in the world where American lives are lost, the thermal weapon will be used without hesitation on one or more of your bodies of water."

General Zaremba reached for her cane and shook it deliberately at Linkum.

"That is a threatening act, not merely a warning. You have graduated a dialogue into a military overture."

She got to her feet and looked directly at him.

He stood up too. "It was not intended to be hostile

in any way, Madame Zaremba. If I chose my words badly, they are mine, not his. Chorley emphasized that he was addressing you on a professional plane in the field of intelligence, that he had the highest respect for your abilities, and that the purpose of this approch was peaceful and preventative."

"In that case, Mr. Linkum, he should have put those sentiments into his document and signed his name."

She appeared to compose herself after the outburst; how much of it was genuine and how much play-acting to get a rise out of him—and more information—he couldn't be sure.

He added, "I can say this for myself: If the purpose of this encounter was to increase instead of to prevent the risk of further warlike acts, I would not be involved."

Madame Zaremba smiled and extended her hand.

"It was a pleasure to meet you and have this important exchange of views with someone who wears the Order of Suvorov in his jacket."

He'd at least remembered to do that.

"If in your haste you were not able to obtain museum postcards, we shall be glad to mail them to you."

Zaremba was signaling strength, letting him know that she knew that he had not come all this way to get frivolous coded cablegrams from Baltimore, Maryland.

"I sincerely trust, Madame Zaremba, that we can meet again under other circumstances."

"I would not be too surprised if we do, Mr. Linkum. Someday, somewhere."

Afterward, they said that all of northern Europe was hemorrhaging. It had not stormed and thundered with such intensity for a decade. Streams of soaked debris skittered along the gutters, clogging drains and rising over the stoops of houses, forming tributaries in the streets of the cities. From the Gulf of Finland through the Baltic and North Seas to the English Channel, waves crashed along the shorelines and even powerful nuclear-fueled dreadnoughts and submarines were locked into home ports. Sea and land traffic stalled, and fog billowed and descended, lowering visibility and socking in the international airports. Nothing moved.

To Linkum, it appeared that the weather had conspired against him. His emergency orders were to rush home with the postcards: himself. Something was in the air, but he was grounded. He wished the hell that Chorley had not been so cryptic; that they had worked out a set of contingency messages in blind code. It could have been simple—single, double and triple digits that stood for prearranged meanings, the sort they'd once used between them that he hadn't forgotten and were impossible to decode.

Instead, he found himself sitting in the Audley Pub on Mount Street in London's W1 country for the second day, waiting for the skies to open so that he could make it back to the States. Luckily, he had caught a KLM freighter flight after midnight at Sheremetievo Airport. General Zaremba, even dealing with a foreign carrier, had demonstrated her muscle on her home ground. When he declined her invitation to spend some time in Moscow she had lifted the phone, spoken a few curt words and the KLM flight was held until he had turned up on the runway. In Amsterdam he waited for a few hours and then had taken the only plane, a British Airways, still moving westward. At Heathrow all the electronic billboard postings said: Delayed. Why had Chorley wanted him to use an American carrier? For security—or for the Pentagon bookkeepers? He figured that he might as well stand by in the relative comfort of London than hang around the airport waiting for reassuring announcements. He started to place a call to Chorley but some old instinct told him to maintain silence while aboard; not to leave a spoor.

He remembered an anonymous bed-and-breakfast in a mews off South Audley Street, and they remembered him and found a dormered room below the attic, if he wouldn't mind. He wouldn't. It was not the splendid, low-key Connaught, where he would stay once in a while after covering some dust-up in a corner of the world, but it was only a few blocks down the street, close enough to call up memories, to envision Jennie with him in one of the high-ceilinged, blue-wallpapered rooms. He bathed, drying himself with a towel heated on a civilized iron rack, and felt at home after the chilling air of Muscovy.

In the Audley Pub he ate lunch standing in the gilt and velvet buffet bar—ox-tongue and cucumber sandwiches with creamy black stout Guinness—and peered through the jeweled cut-glass windows at the banked fog that enveloped the street. A crush of bodies ebbed and flowed around the bar. He walked outside, orienting himself, and stopped at the stationer's shop on the corner for a lined noteblock.

With time to kill he decided to write down everything he could remember about his encounter with Zaremba: every question and response, physical descriptions of her somber companions, times to determine distances between airports and their meeting-place, like measuring the azimuth from a reference-point to an artillery target, even the details of the Mig. He knew Chorley would want such information. A nursery rhyme circled around his mind: *Little Tommy Tucker, sang for his supper* . . . . He could not remember the rest; no matter, it was kid stuff, yet somehow appropriate just now.

He did not want to return to the room below the attic, and would have preferred to sit in one of the deep chairs past the concierge's desk at the Connaught, but there was always the chance of running into some American correspondent or well-heeled publisher there, requiring explanations. Instead, he strolled down Carlos Place and entered the open iron portals of St. George's Hanover Square Gardens. At one end of the half-hidden private park, fitting in unobtrusively, stood the Farm Street Church of the Immaculate Conception, a venerable gray stone structure punctuated by a rose window that was served by the Jesuits. At the other end, in a rambling red-brick Victorian building, stood the South Audley Street District Library, run by the City of Westminster. A flock of pigeons rose to their dovecotes on the ledges of the smoke-brick apartment houses when he sat down in their territory on one of the wooden benches that bore the names of the donors. The nameplate on his bench read, "Presented by two American ladies who loved this garden." Whenever he passed through London he always tried to find a few moments to pause in the ancient greensward. The benches and pathways and blooming flowers held memories of a visit with Elena and Tony, long ago—two or three lives ago.

In the middle of the afternoon the library was usually crowded with housewives and clerks working in the neighborhood who dropped in to return and collect a week's reading. But they had not ventured forth in the inclement weather. Linkum climbed the steps, past the unlocked bicycles, and checked the catalogues for books on Moscow and Leningrad. He picked a handful of volumes off the shelves, including an atlas, and began to make notes. For more than an hour he wrote steadily, surprised that he had so much to recollect and regretting that he had not carried a hidden tape recorder to match those in General Zaremba's elegant ballroom. But that would have been playing their game; on second thought, he was glad that he had entered and left the Soviet Union with nothing more than his professional experience, silently recording what counted and filtering out extraneous sounds. The John Bartholomew maps in *The Times Concise Atlas* were scaled too small, but he was sure that Chorley's cartographers would be able to determine the exact location of Zaremba's headquarters in the countryside somewhere outside Moscow.

At dusk he quit the quiet library where no one had questioned his right to read. He sauntered back through the private park. But the gate on the Carlos Place side had been locked for the night. In the dimly lit park, he could see a figure standing in one of the red-painted telephone booths. Nearby, an orange ball of light glowed above the white and baby-blue enameled City of Westminster streetlamps.

In the half-dark he thought he heard footsteps behind him. He could still see the figure in the telephone booth. Someone else had entered the park. Slowing down deliberately, he waited to be overtaken; instead, the alien footsteps slowed to his pace, tracking him.

A weapon. He reached into his pocket for his fountain pen and unscrewed the cap and gripped the pen tightly in his fist. With one swift downward stroke, he remembered, you could pierce an attacker's eyeball and blind him before he could get a shot off.

The notes in his jacket pocket. Burning them would only outline him in the darkness; a moth attracted by a flame. Twenty feet ahead of him, off the pathway, he noticed the lemon-yellow spikes of an azalea bush. Walking toward it, he rolled his notes into a ball, and pretending to smell the blossoms, dropped the notes in the clump of branches at the bottom of the bush.

In the shadows near one of the benches, he imagined a cloaked figure stood observing him. It couldn't have been a reassuring London bobby because the footfalls behind him, starting and stopping, did not have the familiar clunking, hobnailed sound. Someone was after him; otherwise, he would have heard a word of greeting, even a friendly cough.

Don't show fear. Walk slowly. (His mind's-eye turned back in time and he saw the sign again: SLOW 10 M.P.H.—DUST RAISES SHELLS. The sign placed by a British antiaircraft outfit on the country lane south of Pisa. The Germans had an observation post in the Leaning Tower on the northern side of the River Arno. Whenever they spotted the dust kicked up by moving vehicle, an .88 would fire a round at the Anglo-American combat group within their sights. Driving in his jeep, he could see the Germans moving between columns of the Tower. He wanted to reach the farmhouse that served as headquarters, and his instinct was to speed up the lane quickly and get out of their field of vision. But crawl, slow down, show no fear and don't stir up trouble: DUST RAISES SHELLS). . . . After dark, St. George's Hanover Square Gardens was a cul-de-sac. He was at the wrong end, bottled up, walking slowly, deliberately. In, of all places, London.

The Farm Street Church could be a sanctuary if he could make it to the entrance without being attacked by whoever was tailing him. He reached the heavy oak doors and groped along the hinges until his fingers encircled a twisted-iron knocker. Next to it was a small white sign saying PULL. He yanked on the knocker, turning it, but the wooden portals were closed; he began to pound the knocker against the door, hoping to arouse someone inside. The sound of his banging echoed through the garden park. A light appeared in the third floor of a flat facing the church, the window was raised and a voice from on high shouted, "It's bloody shut, you bloody drunk!" The heavy door remained closed. He didn't stand a prayer—bad pun, he thought—of making it into the church.

The figure in the cloak loomed in front of his face,

a large man with a full moustache that curled up at its ends. "I'll trouble you for your papers." The voice was polished but in accented English, cultivated yet foreign. Linkum hesitated for an instant. The large man clawed at his jacket pockets, quickly and professionally, and Linkum lowered his head and butted him in the chest, at the same time swinging his pen weapon in a wide arc to shield himself.

Suddenly he heard another voice shout, "Keep your distance, you bloody bastard . . . " Again, in English, but this one without a trace of an accent. And Linkum now found himself in the middle of a struggle between the tall moustache and a short stocky individual whose face he could not make out. The tall man slid to the ground, grabbing Linkum's leg and trying to pull him down. Linkum kneed him, then stumbling and swinging, hit the ground, and his pen weapon flew out of his hand. He chopped away at themwith only his elbows and knees. In the melee, he couldn't fathom whose side either of them was on but he didn't care to stay there long enough to find out.

The other end of the park near the library exit seemed a good hundred yards away. Untangling himself, crouching low, he made a run for it over the thick cushion of grass and broke out, breathless, at the South Audley Street side.

"Evening, sir—everything all right?"

A bobby stood under the glowing orange streetlamp, a cigarette cuffed in his palm, sneaking a smoke.

"Thank you, officer," he said, trying to catch his

breath. He glanced toward the park, anxious to get away. "I seem to be turned around—could you walk me back to my place?"

He mentioned the mews a few blocks away.

"No problem, sir, I'm going in that direction. A little heavy weather we're having, but it should clear by tomorrow."

The bobby saluted him when they reached the entrance to his Mayfair bed-and-breakfast.

A car behind them slowed down for an instant, then sped away in the darkness.

In the morning the sun uncharacteristically broke through. Linkum got up early and waited for the gate-keeper to arrive on the Carlos Place side of the park. He entered, strolled over to the azalea bush, separated the branches. His ball of notes was gone.

He walked past a signpost for St. George's Hanover Square Gardens that read: "A person shall not in open space wilfully obstruct, disturb, interrupt, or annoy any other person in the use of the open space."

Linkum wondered if he had violated any person's space last night. He had no desire to disturb the peace in the good City of Westminster.

Returning to his bed-and-breakfast he packed up and settled his handwritten bill, promising to return again some time. Hastily, he caught a cab for Heathrow at the stand in front of the Connaught Hotel. Now, for the first time in three days, he saw the familiar silhouette of the city. In the mews, windowboxes were ablaze in a rainbow of flowers; even the overnight refuse was wrapped in colorful sacks of cotton dyed purple; the high-backed Austin taking him to the airport passed in sight of Rotten Row and the horses of the caped ceremonial troopers snorting breaths of steam; over the Serpentine gulls quarreled and wheeled lazily and, a new sight to him in gentlemanly London, joggers monopolizing the Hyde Park roadway and taking their muscles and themselves seriously, just like at home; the taxi passed a sign of progress on a storefront that read, "Pizza on the Park," and then went through Alexandra Gate and onto the Cromwell Road and the M-4, where traffic moved quickly this early in the morning. Passing Hammersmith, he took a last glance at the red-brick chimneys over the rows of narrow houses that had survived the thunder of the Blitz, and he felt nostalgic, as he always did, arriving in or departing London.

All right, American carrier. Okay, Hap, it's your ballgame, and your money. He exchanged his rubles into pounds at Barclay's, then walked to the other side of the airport and exchanged the pounds into dollars at another Barclay's branch, still leaving no traces. He paid for his TWA ticket in cash. The 747 was jammed with backed-up passengers; some had never left the terminal. But his own tardiness paid off when he was kicked up into first-class after all the economy-class seats had been filled.

It was only eleven-thirty in the morning, British time, but the hostess began to pour the champagne for the privileged characters in first moments after they were airborne. Linkum reached into his carrying case for something to read, then realized that he had left his copy of Russian short stories as a present for Andrei and Oriana in Leningrad. He glanced around the cabin. A pile of London newspapers lay unopened beneath the champagne splits and bowls of macadamia nuts. He detached a copy of that morning's *Daily Telegraph*.

Half reading and half nodding from the champagne, he worked his way slowly through the headlines and advice columns: FOG LIFTS OVER NORTH SEA OIL STATIONS . . . BBC BUDGET CUTS REDUCE INCOMES OF AUTHORS AND PLAYWRIGHTS . . . YORKSHIRE MINES STRUCK OVER SAFETY ISSUES . . . ULSTER BULLY BOYS ATTACK ARMY POST IN BELFAST . . . MILLIONARE U. S. PRESIDENT USES CAPITAL GAINS LAW TO AVOID TAXES . . . LIBYAN DICTATOR EMPLOYS FRENCH NUCLEAR EXPERTS . . . WEST END THEATRES RELY ON BROADWAY MUSICALS IN FALL . . . TRIPLE CAPTAIN'S PARADISE DISCOVERED, HUSBAND, KEPT WIVES IN BRIGHTON, MANCHESTER AND BIRMINGHAM . . . PARIS DECREES HIGHER SKIRTS.

Well, the world hadn't changed very much since he had left Washington. Mankind was still hanging in there, bravely and foolishly.

Then a headline on the back news page suddenly stopped him cold It read:

MYSTERIOUS DISAPPEARANCE OF CAUCASIAN LAKE?

The dispatch was attributed to the Reuters news agency but it carried no dateline.

Linkum read the story slowly, down the narrow column:

A Reuters special feature.

Travelers report an unusual occurrence along the Caucasian Riviera in the last forty-eight hours.

Lake Ritsa, a beautiful body of water in the Soviet resort area, suddenly drained out.

"Yesterday the lake was there, and the same evening it disappeared off the face of the earth," a tourist from Stockholm reported.

Soviet officials in Tiflis scoffed at the notion that there was anything unusual. They said this was a "normal" and "natural" incident under certain weather conditions at this time of the year. The officials declared that the lake had similar drainoffs in the past two centuries, according to historical records.

A local Georgian saying goes that the roadway approaches are "as long and twisted as a mother-in-law's tongue." This saying was cited as the reason why the entire resort region for ten miles inland from the former lake has been sealed off from any but official military and police traffic. Tourists in the region have not been permitted to return.

The Caucasian mountain lake once existed 3,000 feet up in the Abkhazia region. It was one and a half miles long, a half-mile across, and it was said to be as deep as it was wide. Lake Ritsa abounded in trout and other game fish. It had once been a favorite resort of Russian aristocrats (boyars). The late Premier Stalin maintained a country home beside the lake.

Foreign tourists reported that flocks of sheep and goats, brought to the Ritsa area for pasture, had been "incinerated" by steam rising from the lake and along its perimeter.

However, regional game and fishery wardens vehemently denied that there had been destruction of flocks or any loss of life. Officials from several agencies in Moscow have arrived in the Caucasian area to take charge, according to well-informed sources.

Linkum signaled the hostess to bring him another split of champagne. Suddenly, he felt like eating and drinking, hoping to keep the suspected truth out of his mind. He looked at his watch and for the third or fourth time, he forgot which, twisted the dial to know whether he was coming or going, awake or asleep. He was somewhere in the middle of the Atlantic, thirty-five thousand feet above the ocean, and he wanted it all to be over with.

He reread the Reuters dispatch line-by-line, measuring the sources and the nuances. He knew the game well; he had covered up and conveyed meanings between the lines himself many times. "Stockholm travelers" and "foreign tourists" and "well-informed sources"—a real pro had put it all together without revealing how and where by a telltale dateline. However, it was out in the open, in the public prints, and that said something too, except, he told himself, he didn't know exactly what. He wondered what the New York and Washington papers had on the same story. Was it a Reuters "special feature" —that was a curious form of credit—instead of a more boastful "exclusive," and which of the intelligence services had served as the leaking conduit? The British had never lost their touch, of that he was certain. As for the French, they were in business for themselves when it came to sharing information; probably no different from his wartime encounters with the *Deuxième Bureau*.

254

Of course, Linkum told himself, it *could* have been something else, a fluke of nature in an area of the world he knew nothing about. Downing the free champagne, flying first cabin in this unreal whale's body miles above the ocean, he replied to his own speculation—not bloody likely.

Still: rush home the bloody postcards. A persistent notion took over his mind, linking the message from Maryland to Lake Ritsa. With half a buzz on, he suddenly, irrelevantly, remembered that he had forgotten to bring Hap Chorley his two boxes of real Havanas from Moscow.

But maybe the big man, blowing smoke rings after dark that night at the Pentagon, didn't deserve them. Cigars or friendship.

The lights were out in nearly every office in the building; the nine-to-five generals and civilian technicians had gone home to their golf and gardens.

Chorley had stopped snapping his fingers nervously. The bourbon had relaxed him after Linkum's glowering return. Now he began to wax philosophical.

"Let me put it this way. The big mistake the Federal Government made around here was changing the name of this place. Department of Defense, my ass. That's hypocrisy. I'm for changing the name back to its real business: war. It would help to wake people up in this town. The Department of War. Because that's just where we're at, chum."

Linkum was not drinking. He kept pressing for answers.

"You screwed me, Hap."

"No, not you. *Them*."

"I was just a cat's-paw in the war games."

"A damn useful one. And you served your country."

"Just a carrier of bullshit messages."

"There I've got to correct you, chum. It wasn't bullshit. It was the goods."

"A fucking pawn."

"Everything in the envelope you gave Zaremba was true, and everything you told her was true. You saw the effects of Operation Stopper with your own eyes."

"In the State of Washington, on an empty lake, not on Lake Ritsa, an inhabited place."

"No one was killed, so far as we can determine. Just a bunch of goats. They took out my listening-posts in Anatolia, and they knocked off my men, not to mention thousands of Turkish peasants. We were just playing by their rules inside their ballpark."

"Including screwing Andrei? You said to speak to him as an old friend. What I did was set him up."

"I'm not worried about Andrei or that woman who works for him, Lhevinne. They're grownups, they've got privileged positions, and they're not our concern. *You* are. That's why I wanted you out of the country before the Chem Warfare people set off our Tinker Toy in the Caucasus."

"But on a *personal* level I gave Andrei the impression—"

"Nothing's personal in the real world, pal, except staying alive, survival. We've given Zaremba and the Russkies a bloody nose they won't forget."

"And how does that help to cool things?"

"It's a warning shot across the bow. We're firing one off from strength, not weakness. We're playing their song and speaking their language—one they understand."

"I seem to have heard that one before, about Vietnam. Destroying the village in order to save it?"

"Nam was chickenshit compared to what's at stake between us nuclear giants. Lake Ritsa has special meaning to them because Uncle Joe helped put it on the map and a lot of the bigshots in the Politburo still have places around there. They tried to play down the news of the lake's disappearance in their controlled newspapers, but the word got around very fast. We made sure of that."

"The Reuters article."

"No problem—we can get stuff on the Reuters wire just like we can get stuff on the American networks with our inside friends. Everybody's got a price, even journalists—they just happen to work a little cheaper than others. Sorry about that. The article has already been passed around by the thousands inside Russia. Zaremba can draw her own conclusions."

Chorley walked over to Linkum and patted his shoulder.

"By the way, I appreciate your written impressions on what you heard and saw there—a fine job, full of detail."

"What do you mean by that?"

Chorley grinned. He reached into his desk drawer, took the rolled-up ball of notes and threw them at Linkum.

"Hap, you almost got me killed—?"

"Saved your ass, to be more accurate. You don't go wandering around parks at night alone in the fog. Not in Central Park or Hanover Square Gardens in London. Still, I must say you gave a pretty good account of yourself, Sam . . . for a guy who's out of practice. You almost tore the skin off my contact there—he's still got ink in his arm from that pen you were swinging."

"Which was your guy—or were they both yours and you were putting on an act to test me in some crazy way—?"

"Hell no, if I couldn't trust you I couldn't trust myself. This was for real. The big guy with the moustache was from one of the Russian intelligence agencies. Not one of Zaremba's men, though. An overzealous character attached to the Soviet trade mission there. I don't know how he got wind of you in London and wanted your report. London's become the new Lisbon, with all the Third World types hot after big bucks and operating from their luxury flats in Kensington, and the moustache has some ties to them too."

"Who was the short guy who tackled him?"

"A Brit. Nice guy, ex-boxer at Queen's College, someone from the old days who does special assignments for us. Once you got out of Moscow, I thought it would be good for your health to have him keep an eye on you."

"He's the one who got my notes and sent them on to you?"

"Right, but the point is this: it confirms that we're on the right track dealing with the Zarembas, tough as they are, because they're not the zealots and cold warriors, the goddamn true believers. They've been through the wars. She faces the same fanatics that I do here, theoreticians and strategists, backed by think tanks, trying to fire up the next Vietnams for the sake of their own macho and careers. Sam, we've got to keep trying, otherwise we'll blow each other up."

Linkum nodded, surprised and pleased that Chorley's words echoed his.

"And next time you're in London, don't try knocking down the church doors or they'll lock you up for sure . . . Now, I'm going to have your notes transcribed for two or three top people, but I'll screen them first and conceal the source. You confirmed some things we already knew and helped to zero in on locales and identities. For your information—not that you'll need it again—that wasn't a KGB setup. It was strictly GRU."

"You're damn right that I won't need it again."

"One never knows," Chorley said. "Anyway, the point is that Zaremba just doesn't collect intelligence—she's operational. *Glavnoye Razvedyvatelnoye Upravlenive.* The GRU is the intelligence directorate on the Soviet General Staff, which makes her even more powerful. She's more than a political cop. You delivered your message to the right person, and place."

"A lot of good it's done. Where's that stalemate?"

"Well, a bloody nose is a helluva lot better than an American broken heart or radiated country . . . Look, I've got something to show you." Chorley twirled the tumblers on his office safe and extracted a set of finely grained blowups.

"Satellite photographs before and after, of Lake Ritsa. Look at the sparkle on the water here. Now, look at this one. The steam rising. And this one. A big nothing of a hole in the ground."

Linkum studied the pictures. They were as clear as the test effects he had seen in Washington.

"We almost didn't get the last shot you're looking at. You want to know why? The Russkies now have an operational land-based laser weapon that is capable of putting one of our low-orbiting satellites like the one that took these pictures out of action. It's a charged particle beam that works like a bolt of lightning. Zap, you're dead."

Chorley pointed his lit cigar at Sam. "The Russkies reacted a little too slowly this time because we caught them with their pants down. Otherwise, our satellite would have been just another chunk of debris orbiting in that great junkyard in the sky."

"Am I supposed to know about their laser?" Linkum asked.

"You never heard it from me. The same goes for the rest of what you've seen in the last few days. Incidentally, I trust you didn't mind my upgrading you to first class on the flight home. You deserved it."

"You think of everything, don't you?"

260

"Not quite, but I try to cover the ass of my people. You look pooped. I suppose you'd rather return to New York. I've got my friendly little bomber standing by if—"

"No, thanks—not even the Eastern shuttle. I've had enough of that stuff. I'm taking a train."

Chorley nodded. "You're quite a guy. I hope there are no hard feelings, Sam."

Linkum shrugged. "I wouldn't bet on my feelings, Hap."

Eight

Under a lambent sky two hundred miles beyond the Montauk rip, the U.S.S. *Cuttlefish*, spray raking her uncovered forward deck guns, sliced through a sea of white horses, tracking the Soviet intelligence trawler *Glinka*.

But it was too late, and now only thoughts of vengeance rode the high waves.

The Montauk Lighthouse, once a proud sentinel signaling the first ray of hope on the approaches to the New World, lay shattered in a thousand pieces. It had stood watch on the Long Island promontory for nearly two centuries. Now, above the bloodstained soil and sand, gulls wheeled and sideslipped into the reddened waters, brushing their wings over the entrails of Coast Guardsmen and fishermen whose bodies rolled in the foam along the shoreline.

At the moment that the Lighthouse had cracked open and tumbled down the cliffs, a pleasure boat, *Saucy Queen II*, passed beneath. It was bound for its anchorage around Gin Beach in a beer-can port but never reached home. For huge boulders long held in place by the natural balance of dune grass and rock suddenly became unhinged. Spinning and picking up speed, the boulders struck the thin-skinned vessel, skewering and sinking her. Then shards of glass from the Lighthouse sailed straight and true against the broken deck, tearing open the flesh of those on board. The sea washed over the stunned victims, filling their lungs in the deathly claiming waters.

The first word of alarm was telephoned by an alert woman corporal on duty at the Seven Hundred and Seventy-third Air Force radar station that was concealed behind a stand of pitch pines within sight of the Lighthouse. She called the commander of the Shinnecock Coast Guard station in Hampton Bays, who immediately ordered one of his three Reliance class cutters to change course and head for the Point. The airman or rather airperson, as the young corporal preferred to be known, was going by the book for the Lighthouse Service came under the Coast Guard. The initial sighting of the destruction from above was made by a hovering Coast Guard helicopter on loan from an Army Reserve unit that had been disbanded for lack of volunteers. Later, a jurisdictional dispute arose between the Air Force and Navy, which controlled the Coast Guard in times of national distress, about who could claim credit for the responses to the disaster and who was in charge. To help defuse the inter-service rivalry, Washington awarded Bronze Stars to the enlisted persons involved and Silver Stars to their officers at headquarters.

Inevitably, rumors raced up and down the villages in the Hamptons. Someone reported that he had heard from a volunteer fireman who worked at the A&P that the fireworks stored for the Fourth of July celebration had ignited and caused the Lighthouse to go up like a Roman candle. Old year-round residents said that the destruction resulted from a freak tidal wave that reminded them of the big hurricane of '38, and the effect would be to depress the resale value of their homes. Topless renters from the wilds of Manhattan, forbidden to do their thing on the public beaches controlled by the township, were blamed because a lot of them hung out near the Lighthouse after dark, smoking pot, lighting fires illegally and carrying on generally. Someone, a die-hard Roosevelt hater, declared that the Lighthouse had been pulverized by a buried bomb from the Second World War that had been overlooked in the stupid haste to disarm the United States because Franklin D. Roosevelt had sold out to Joe Stalin at Yalta.

In less than two hours, the true significance of the fall of the Montauk Lighthouse had been surmised by the Joint Chiefs at the Pentagon. Standoff or shootout? They had figured the chances to be fifty-fifty after their own operation in the Caucasus. So far it was the wrong fifty.

Hap Chorley and his Army and Navy opposite-numbers on the National Security Agency's top intelligence command confirmed their suspicions when ELINT picked up heavy traffic from the *Glinka* in the waters off Long Island to GRU headquarters in Moscow. The interceptions were decoded, matched against voice-tapes in computers, and the messages came through loud and clear: the mission against the Montauk Lighthouse had been brought to a successful conclusion exactly as planned.

After an oral briefing, the "President's-Eyes-Only" memorandum from the Joint Chiefs summed up the situation:

"The geological fault in the earth plates beneath the Montauk promontory was widened by remote control on command of the operational trawler *Glinka*. It is an intelligence collector of the Primorye class with built-in computer analysis capability. Methodology is not yet known at DOD, but it is assumed that the fault was triggered by laser beam.

"On balance, GRU does not as yet know methodology of ChemWar thermal weapon that took out Lake Ritsa. There are several thousand similar faults (see Supplement One) subject to attack all over coastal United States. There are hundreds of large, vulnerable bodies of water (Supplement Two) located inside Soviet Union."

Even after the *Glinka* turned northward for a triumphant voyage across the ocean to her Baltic Sea port, the *Cuttlefish* rode shotgun behind the Soviet intelligence trawler all the way to the English Channel. There her track was picked up by British destroyers and monitored by special arrangement between the Allied intelligence services. To circle the coastal waters of the United States and make sure that no Soviet surface vessel penetrated the newly designated five hundred-mile limit, American naval vessels from the Pacific and Indian Ocean fleets were brought home. The cover story was to protect American commerical fisherman from having the rich waters around the country depleted by foreign fishermen. Commerical fishing by most of the nations, friendly and otherwise, almost came to a halt as a result of the frequent boarding inspections; in retaliation, American fishing trawlers were stopped on foreign fishing-banks.

What could not be publicly admitted, by either government, was that the Soviets had commited a full second-strike act of war on American ground in response to a semi-first-strike act inside Russian territory; that because the Soviet strike in Turkey had been against an American ally and American personnel equipment, even if not actually on American territory; the fact was that Russia had bared its teeth first. But to reveal the actual course of events would encourage the flaming warriors of both sides, itching to let loose their intercontinental ballistic missiles. To them, the Hap Chorleys and, if they knew of them, the Sam Linkums on the outside were suspect—not to be trusted on the top rungs of the escalation ladder. And they were right to think so.

The conjurers in the press delivered their Lighthouse stories for the feature-minded newspapers and the networks broadcast their lighthearted anecdotes between commercials. And the preachers preached of God's will. *Te Deum.*

The Federal authorities decided not to replace the Montauk Lighthouse, declaring it to be too costly and a relic of another age. Instead, lights would be strung on the oil rigs in the seas surrounding Long Island that had been leased for ninety-nine-year terms by a consortium of Mobil and Exxon. The oil companies announced that, as a public service, they would contribute matching funds to build a fine plaque to commemorate the spot where the Lighthouse had once stood.

On the beach below, Montauk residents combed the sand for bits of Lighthouse glass. The shards were mounted on scallop shells and turned into ashtrays. Souvenir stores in East Hampton offered them for sale as historic collectibles, with only a little less reverence than pieces of the True Cross, to tourists and renters. On Independence Day a portion of the proceeds of the Lighthouse ashtray sales was donated to the Ladies Village Improvement Society to keep up their good arboreal works.

Nine

"I'VE HAD IT," Jennie said. "You don't have to say yes, but I'd like you to come by for the farewell drink to the section."

"I haven't been inside the building for months," Sam said.

"I know it'll be uncomfortable but you started the damn section, you were its first editor, and some of the guys asked me to ask you if you wanted to show up."

"Have they been let go by Her Highness?"

"Not exactly. They've been given the option of staying on and working on the expanded *Lifestyles* section or writing news bulletins off the wires for the network affiliates."

"Did she offer you the same opportunity?"

"I never listened long enough to know. I was summoned to Ms. Delafield's fur-lined office at the network knowing that the Sunday news roundup section was about to be killed. The others had already been told. The moment she started to talk about the bottom line, I told her to shove it."

"Well, well . . . just like that?"

"Just like that. Someone I admire very much had done the same thing. I knew the script."

"Thank you, but what I did I did for myself. I wasn't telling anyone else to follow me over the side."

"I'm not anyone else, Sam. I'm part of a third force: us. We've created a whole other entity."

"Jennie," he said, reaching across the table for her hand and brushing his lips across her fingers. "Darling Jennie."

They were sitting in their corner at Mannie's Place, catching up. Linkum had not explained his latest absence; she knew him well enough to respect his silences.

He ordered two more on-tap Carlsbergs. "When is this little shindig supposed to take place?"

"Now—whenever we show up. It's nothing fancy. We've finished our pieces for the Sunday paper and just have to check the proofs."

"Will Delafield or any of the network people be there?"

"Are you kidding? We're nonpersons now, occupying valuable corporate real estate. So much per foot. No, Sam, all that's left of our relationship with the people crosstown is the nuisance of paperwork. It's an implied trade off—don't make waves about killing the news analysis section and you'll get a more generous severance settlement in your final pay packet. They haven't put it quite that bluntly but that's the meaning of the golden handshake."

"They still want it both ways, don't they? To be loved, or at least not to be publicly embarrassed."

"Will you come along?" she said quietly.

"Sure, but I really feel strange about going on the premises."

They walked to the paper. It was past the commuting hour and not too many people were around. The trucks were beginning to roll with the early-run sections, and Linkum remembered the strange division that existed between the editorial and mechanical people, each regarding the other as Calibans. In the reception area, he felt at home again.

"How they hanging, Lou?"

"Hanging loose, Sam. Good to see you."

No word of other yesterdays. At least they had not fired some of the old retainers who had been aroud when he had first arrived, long ago; who told you they liked stories you wrote after returning from a faraway assignment.

The news analysis writers greeted him warmly, sensing that it had taken some effort to show up. They kidded about past headlines with double-entendres that had got by him and about his big blue pencil on their copy. No one asked what he was up to. Casually, he enquired if they planned to move elsewhere, and he was pleased when the writers said they would probably give it a whirl in the *Lifestyles* section. Laughing in the dark, the writers said that a professional could insinuate hard facts when nobody was looking. Linkum told them they were doing the right thing to stay on; you never could tell when the next palace revolution would break out at the network and someone up there made the astonishing discovery that readers really wanted to know what was going on in the world and maybe news could sell.

Quietly, Jennie stepped away and checked one of her stories, and he marveled now as when he had first observed her, looking calm in the hurricane of words. To the others, she made no gesture of bravado about her own departure. They all knew about the obligations that tied you to steady paychecks—the alimony payments, the college tuitions and home mortgages, the deaths in the family. So they drank their last drinks from plastic paper cups filled with liquor furtively locked up in desk drawers and watched for the magical moment when the copyboy brought the first printed sections up from the rumbling press room. Turning first to their own stories, then going over the whole section for last-minute catches, they folded the sections carefully and took an extra few copies, aware this would be the last one they would put out. They said their goodnights and good-byes, ending it before they became morbid, and went their separate ways.

Departing, Jennie turned to Sam and said, "May I invite you to my place, sir? I promise to behave myself."

He said, "I make no such promises for myself."

From her apartment overlooking Gramercy Park he followed the patterns of light cast by the street lamps and by the towering luxury buildings that loomed in the semi-darkness. The dwellers of the studios were home in their small apartments; the highest floors were away for the summer in the Hamptons. And on Montauk Point, no Lighthouse sent out its ancient candlepower. His mind wandered, crossing oceans.

Jennie came up behind him and her arms encircled his waist. He started to turn but she told him not to move, that she just wanted to hold him close.

"What are you thinking about at this very second?" she asked, and he told her, "That there are one billion Chinese and eight hundred million Malaysians and how come I fell in love with you?" She said, "You left out a few billion people, but who's counting?" He said, "I'd rather be here with you than anywhere in the world." She said, "Will you always be my best friend?" He asked, "What are the requirements?" and she replied, "Well, a best friend is someone you share your crayons with and always talk to, even when you're angry." He said, "Even when the other person has done something wrong?" And she said, "Especially then."

He locked his hands behind her pressing body without turning, and said, "Because in these last few weeks, I may have done something wrong or maybe just dumb."

Jennie said, "If you want to, tell me about it."

"I know that I've been behaving strangely, disappearing, but I don't think I want to talk about it. Not right now. Sometime."

"Up to you, Sam."

He turned away from the window and kissed her forehead.

"If it's up to a best friend, I have a wonderful idea. Let's go to your bedroom, friend."

"I never thought you'd ask. Your robe is hanging in its regular place in my closet, darling."

Before making love, he carefully kissed the scar below her shoulder blade.

Afterward, he felt a dampness on her cheek and heard her crying in the darkness.

"Will you promise to kiss me before I die?"

"Don't talk that way, Jennie."

"I'm sorry, but sometimes I think about dying when I'm together with you and so happy. I never want us to end."

"What we have, won't, even when we're apart . . ." He hesitated, then said, "More than anything else, I wish I could give you the one thing I can't, my name. For whatever it's worth."

Jennie lowered her head to his chest. "I know that, Sam. God knows, I've thought about it often enough. But if having your name was the only thing that mattered, you wouldn't be here with me. Even with tears, I'm a big girl."

"I wanted you to know I think about it."

"That's good," she said, recovering, "because it makes two of us."

She flicked on the television set to catch the late news and to see if any of her final stories would be affected. Sam told her not to worry, that major developments didn't occur Saturday night because even the lowliest government officials had learned to time their pronunciamentos to make the major network shows.

"I suppose that one or both of us will have to think about other things too," she said. "Like getting a job and making a living or making a living and getting a job.

Personally, I'd prefer to be a philanthropist and give it away."

"Let's not be too realistic tonight," he said. "You know, I once had an old Russian friend during the war —I think I've mentioned him to you—who used to speak in epigrams. Now and then, I recall some of them. Like one about doctors, that what patients needed most of all was *a tincture of time*. It was the most important medicine. Well, after the shock of being run over by a network conglomerate, and so forth we could both use some healing time—just a tincture."

Jennie nodded, and said, "What happens after then, Sam?"

"I've been thinking that it would be possible to take a step forward by taking a step backward. There are small papers all over the country, in towns of every size, that could use professionals. They've got their problems and own set of pressures but I've read some edited by friends of mine that are first-rate, professional. It might even be feasible to start a small paper and make a big noise in your pond or acquire an interest in one in exchange for your skills. I guess it would even be possible to make a living teaching journalism somewhere but I don't want to get off the firing line, not with all the things happening in the world."

Jennie said, "Not teaching, not for either of us. You've got too much to say, and dammit, so have I. You've got to have a forum."

"That's a fancy word for it. I prefer soapbox. That's what it should be all about—broadsides in the night without the bullshit called objectivity. After all, that's

275

how it all began, having your independence in print and letting the other fellow have his. Tom Paine never wrote 'But on the other hand . . . ' We've seen what's happened to most of the big press. It's been tainted by the same hard-sell bland that rules the tube. End of speech."

Jennie laughed. "That's the most I've heard you say in a month. Wherever you land, do you think you'll find a place for a best friend?"

Sam pulled her closer to him.

"Only if you bring along your crayons," he said.

The late news ended with a home team anecdote, delivered in machine gun rat-a-tat-tat by a head in a razor-cut haircut wearing a green sports jacket, who was paid a half-millon dollars a year to read. Then the commercials came on for the vitamin-enriched animal dinners. In a chorus line of color, the animals danced happily across the screen to their feeding trays. The world was sponsored by High Protein Dog Meal, Good Mews and Little Friskies. The weather was also for sale to the highest bidder. Before turning off the TV set, Jennie and Sam and the rest of the country watched as the singing animals mouthed a tune:

> *"Little Friskies, Little Friskies,*
> *Ain't we got fun???*
> *Little Friskies, Little Friskies,*
> *Ain't we got fun!!!"*

No pet would go hungry in America tomorrow.

A week later, the telephone rang early in the morning just when Sam Linkum was leaving his apartment to

276

do some research in the library and follow a routine: combing the newspapers for buried items about so-called natural disasters and environmental accidents anywhere in the world.

"It's Maryjane? You remember me, Mr. Linkum, now don't tell me otherwise?"

The voice was familiar, Southern-seductive, but he couldn't recall it until she said, in her rising inflection, "Air Force? Pentagon?" It was the body outside Hap's door.

"Of course I remember you, Maryjane. I hope you're well."

"Couldn't be better. It's so good to hear your voice, Mr. Linkum. We hope we're not disturbing you? Now you have a nice day for yourself, and here is the boss-man."

Chorley got on the line.

"Sam, Hap here. Everything going along okay, chum?"

He told him he was waiting for the apocalypse but that, otherwise, everything was okay. They had not spoken since his report and cool departure.

"Just checking to see that all was well with you."

"That all, Hap?"

"Well, there is something else, if you have a moment. You working?"

"On my own. In fact, I'm finishing a piece for one of the opinion weeklies about a rival organization of yours—the Arms Control and Disarmament Agency and some of the things they're working on."

"If I told you that I was all for the ACDA as long

as what they're shooting for isn't unilateral disarmament, you wouldn't be too surprised, I hope. The trouble is, they're not very effective in this town."

"That's what I plan to write. One reason why is that the lobby for armaments is a hundred or a thousand times stronger and richer than the voices for disarmament."

"You've got a point there, pal."

Linkum heard a loud noise, and then the phone dropping. A moment later, Chorley muttered, "Dammit, just kicked over the ashtray again, clumsy jerk." Linkum laughed for the first time, and Chorley added, "I didn't say for you to agree."

"Well, Hap, give it to me straight—what did you have in mind?"

"An assignment. Nothing like the other. I think you'd find it interesting."

"Stop right there—not a chance."

"It's more of a diplomatic effort—"

"Sorry, the Guardi Art Company is out of business. *Finito.* Let me ask you something, if it's no great military secret. Have you heard anything about Andrei?"

"Indirectly, yes. My information is that Glazunov is no longer affiliated with the Hermitage but I don't know where he is."

"Maybe they have a museum in the Gulag," Linkum said bitterly. "Did your people pick up anything about Lhevinne?"

"They let her out after he was removed. She's on the waiting list in Bucharest and should get to Israel in a few months. That's not for publication, of course."

"At least she's starting a new life."

"You're sure you don't want to come down here so I can explain what I have in mind face-to-face?"

"You'd be wasting your time."

"All right, Sam, I'm not going to twist your arm." He paused. "I'm still grateful for what you did—the way you carried off an honorable assignment. A *very* honorable assignment. And remember, they pulled a fast one on us—Turkey came before our action. We, you, negotiated in good faith. And we're still trying . . . Well, let me know if I can be of help to you personally sometime, chum."

Linkum said thanks. He was about to hang up when something occurred to him.

"There is one thing that's very personal. I don't know if you can do anything about it, but it involves Graves Registration and the Quartermaster General. Before Elena took sick, we often talked about getting our son reburied. She hoped that Antonio could be in Italian soil, and I agreed with her for sentimental reasons. We wanted his remains moved from Pinelawn to the American military cemetery above the Anzio beachhead, near Nettuno. But the red tape got so thick that we stopped trying. She's incapable of acting now, but I still feel an obligation to carry out her wishes."

"Consider it done, Sam," Chorley said. He heaved a deep sigh from the pit of his chest. "Dammit to hell, I'm sorry about your boy."

There was once a battle in their war at a place called Anzio along the coastline between Naples and Rome but it was not a famous victory and that cold winter and

279

spring men died in the mud and rain listening to a dirge of thundering shellfire. Millennia ago other soldiers in armor under the Franks and Goths and Romans had perished and fertilized the same ground and no markers or military cemeteries on the high ground commemorated their forgotten causes.

They killed so primitively then: without napalm, without the benefit of the latest inventions in physics and chemistry and the modern sciences for the greater glory, amen.

The green Graves Registration covered pickup truck was waiting on the far end of the Italian Air Force aerodrome north of Naples when the American Air Transport Command cargo plane lowered the aluminum coffin to the ground. Gently, the army corporal in charge lifted the coffin with the help of three civilians and slid it into the truck and dropped the tarpaulin. An old Plymouth stood by with a chauffeur in an incongrous black cap over his polo shirt waiting to drive him behind the pickup to the cemetery grounds. But Linkum declined and instead remained with the coffin, as he had done from Farmingdale and across the Atlantic to here, alone with his son.

Everything had been arranged in advance. The civil service caretaker of the Sicily-Rome Memorial Cemetery outside Nettuno greeted Linkum, expressing disappointment that his personal car and chauffeur had not been used, but he was glad that what he kept referring to as "the remains" had arrived "safe and sound." Linkum asked if there had been any similar reburials. The caretaker said it was unusual because nearly all of the 7,862 Americans under the crosses and Stars of David had fallen in the campaigns in Sicily and southern Italy. But special permission had been granted to a few families that had suffered deaths in Korea and Vietnam and wished to be reunited in the same cemetery. In the next-of-kin room adjacent to the chapel the caretaker asked Linkum to sign a receipt acknowledging that the remains had been delivered in good order; and then he added how burdened he was with paperwork. Linkum glared at the obsequious caretaker and scrawled his signature. Everything mortal was a job to someone.

Antonio's coffin was set down within the peristyle that enclosed the colonnaded marble monument to the missing. Then the caretaker went to lunch. Linkum stood next to the coffin, waiting alone. In a few moments the priest arrived from Nettuno. He was gray, thin and dignified.

"I am Father Grondoni," he said in almost faultless English. Black wing-tipped shoes showed below his cassock. "I was informed that you had requested a minister be present at the burial."

"Minister or priest—I didn't specify," Linkum said. "I just told the caretaker that I would appreciate it if a few words were spoken in the traditional way. My wife was, still is, Italian, but she is unable to be here. My son was killed in Vietnam. None of us, I'm afraid, were churchgoers. Your English is excellent."

"I was a liaison officer with the Anglo-Americans during the war—the partisans in this area were under my command before I joined the church. I had many friends. Some are here."

"I was around these parts too in that war," Linkum said. "One of my closest friends was killed during the landings at Anzio. I once laid a wreath on his grave here, years ago. My wife wanted our son interred in Italian soil."

"Sentiment needs no explanations," Father Grondoni said. "I am sorry to hear of your misfortune. Let us proceed."

The open ground in a row that was shaded by umbrella pines awaited Antonio's coffin. The three Italian workmen lowered the coffin by thick ropes, and then began to spade the earth over it. One of them brought over a motorized mechanical digger to shovel the earth but the priest, noticing Linkum's expression, pushed him aside. Instead, he took one spade and handed the other to Linkum.

"It is right to bury your own dead," Father Grondoni said. "The work is not for strangers." Together, the priest and the father covered the coffin while the workmen stood by, regarding them with curiosity. The priest labored with his hands alongside Linkum. His cassock became fringed with fresh brown earth. After they finished and the burial mound was level with the grass, Linkum turned to thank the priest. But no words came out of his mouth. He heard his voice choking, and then he began to cry.

Father Grondoni came over to his side of the grave and put his arm around Linkum's shoulder.

"It is right for the soul to cry," the priest said. "God grieves."

Linkum closed his eyes and attempted to seal the tears that had broken out of his storage of memory. His brow furrowed into thoughts of the past, and Antonio's youth passed across his mind, and the boy became younger and younger, until they were walking together, with Antonio taking his first tentative steps, and falling, and getting up again, and always the child's fingers were entwined in his, trustingly.

In the reverie, Linkum clenched his fingers tightly in his palms and then felt his hands being pried open and soothed. He opened his eyes, and Father Grondoni's bony strong hands covered his, and the priest half-whispered, "*Coraggio*, Linkum, *coraggio, coraggio.*"

And still holding his hands, Father Grondoni lowered his head and recited, "O God, give us grace, we beseech thee, to entrust the soul of this child, Antonio Linkum, to thy never-failing care and love, and bring us all to thy heavenly kingdom. Father of mercies and giver of all comfort, deal graciously, we pray thee, with all those who mourn this child's name, that, casting every care on thee, they may know the consolation of thy love, Amen."

Linkum formed an "Amen" on his lips, and Father Grondoni nodded reassuringly and said, "In sure and certain hope of the Resurrection to eternal life, we commit the body of this child to the ground. The Lord bless him and keep him, the Lord make his face to shine upon him and be gracious unto him, the Lord lift up his countenance upon him, and give him peace, both now and forevermore. Amen."

"Yes," Linkum said softly, glancing at the mound of earth covering Antonio, "this is his peace."

"Amen," Father Grondoni repeated.

"Amen," Linkum said, turning his head away.

An old woman in mourning black, hobbling with a cane, came up the aisle where they stood, crossed herself, and closed her eyes for a moment. She held out two wreaths of yesterday's faded, bloodless roses. Linkum took them and pressed all the dollars in his pocket into her gnarled hands. Then he bent low and placed a wreath on his son's grave.

They walked out of the shade of the pines and locust past rows of white marble tombstones lined up like soldiers on parade. Linkum led Father Grondoni toward the oldest section of the cemetery. He halted before a Star of David. Below it was carved:

S-SGT. SAUL A. BORKEN
HQ. 5TH WING, AIR CORPS
FEB. 13, 1920-FEB. 12, 1944

Linkum placed the second wreath of roses on the cared grass against the marble marker.

Father Grondoni asked him, "Did you know this one?" and Linkum replied, "An old friend—we once had much in common."

"If you wish," the priest said, "I can recite the Kaddish."

Linkum nodded.

The priest tood a prayer book from the folds of his cassock and read the mourning words carefully in Hebrew. Then he translated: "Magnified and sanctified be the glory of God, in the world created according to His will. May His sovereignty soon be acknowledged, during our lives and the life of all Israel. Let us say, Amen."

Linkum added, "Amen."

Leaving, Father Grondoni brushed aside a proffered contribution. "From an old partisan with a good memory," the priest said, extending his hand.

Alone, Sam Linkum walked toward the high green knoll commanding the planted fields of the cemetery. Behind him a blue haze filtered violent shades of chiaroscuro across the scarred Alban Hills. Gazing at the caverns in the earth and the headstones of Nettuno, his eyes narrowed and dimmed. Beyond the tranquil Tyrrhenian Sea, sophisticated weapons ruled the oceans and roamed the heavens with new burnt offerings for the ancient gods.

After all this time, he had found that he could still be touched with a noble anger: to have tried instead of standing was a kind of decency. The effort to brake the dying time over the horizon could go on. Dammit, in his own cockeyed way Hap Chorley had tried to break through the battlements of irrationality around him. Close, but no cigar . . . Still, he knew he would have to be part of it. In the roseate light of that late afternoon, Linkum had no regrets about being a man engaged again.